MUSEPAPER 1.0

VOLUME ONE

2019

MUSEPAPER 1.0 is dedicated to these submitting poets and writers:

Michael A.
Anwar A.
Coranna A.
Hillary A.
Pernille D.
Maryann A.
Cezanne A.
Jason Al-S.
Howard A.
David A.
Mary A.
Caroline A.
Candace A.
Adrianne A.
Heather A.
Carrie B.
Brenda B.
Margaret B.G.
Susan B.S.
Ariel B.
Lauren B.
George B.
Helen B.L.
Elaine B.
Ranald B.
John B.
Elaine B.
E.B. B.
Alison B.
Babette B.
Melissa B.
Betsy B.
Manuella B.
Jane B.
Jerri B.
Kentrell B.
Carol B.
Creighton B.
Nancy B.
Maame B.
Kelli B.
Jodie B.
Susan B.
Eric B.
Tom B.
Anne B.
Sylvia B.
Jude B.
Melody B.G.
Jessica B.
Micheal B.
Morgan B.
Sandra B.
Gloria B.
Rebecca B.
Lynne B.
Teresa B.
Vanessa B.
Marylou B.
Lawrence C.
Kelly C.

Kelli C.
Emily C.
Rachelle C.
Constance C.
Leslie C.
John C.
Elisa C.
Alex C.
Johnson C.
Deborah C.
Robert C.
Marlene C.
Charles C.
Kathy C.
James C.
William C.
G.L. C.
Mary Ann C.
Charles C.
PS C.
Edie C.K.
Randy Cox
Mikey C.
Victoria C.
Sean C.
Jordan C.
Shawn C.
Earl C.
Nancy D.
Marcy D.
Janine D.
Paul D.
Jackie D. M.
Annie D.
Ginger D.
Timothy D.
Deborah D.
JP D.
Sally D.
Sahil D.
Heather D.
Gail D.
Patricia D.
Libby D.
Andrew D.
Beth D.
Micah E.
Michael T. E.
Myles E.
Laura E.
Lois E.
Wilson E.
Howard E.
Jessica E.
Meredith E.
Brian F.
Daniel F.
Victoria F.
Michele F.
Stuart F.
Jaclyn F.

Joyce F.
Melissa F.
Paula F.
Keith Mark G.
Nina G.
Kathryn G.
Tina G.
Janet G.
Clare G.
Adrienne G.
Amy G.
Richard G.
Howard G.
Eileen G.
Samuel G.
Judith G.C.
Linda G.
Lisa G.
Sharon G.
Melissa G.
Catherine G.
Sharon G.
Susan G.
Christina G.
John G.
Christopher G.
Mark G.
Shayna G.
Rowan G.
Chris G.
Jason H.
Liezel M. H.
Tresha H.
Megan H.
Gilliam H.
Christine H.
John, Jr H.
Renee H.
MiChael H.
Courtney H.
Georganne H.
Lyall H.
Janelle H.
James H.
Marina H.
Hozefa H.
Elizabeth H.
Gloria H.
Becky H.
Lori H.
Jacqueline H.
Eileen H.G.
Dennis H.
Allison H.T.
John H.
Elizabeth H.
Lisa H.
Diane H.
Conor H.M.
Heidi H.
Mary Beth H.

Bill H.
Eric I.
Aletha I.
Alaina I.
Martin I.
Robert I.
Trish Lindsey J.
Duncan J
Thomas J.
Cameron J.
Thomas J.
Marilyn J.
Joy J.
Paulette J.
Charlie J.
Anoop J.
Kate K.
Daria K.
MinSoo K.
Lorelei K.
Mary K.
Ellen K.
Yoon-Chan K.
Evelyn K.
M. Kite
Suzanne M. K.
Ren K.
Jen K.
Joanna K.
John K.
Stephanie K.
Sandra K.
Robert K.
Harry K.
Evelyn K.
Olaf K.
Wendy K.
Thom K.
Elizabeth K.
Judy L.
Paul L.
Lee L.
Jennifer L.
Jacqueline L.
Stacey L.
Lamoureaux L.
Megan L.
Paul L.
Karen L.
Mitch L.
Lori L.
Jan L.
Sabrina L'H.
Rachel L.
Hsu Tai L.
Ellaraine L.
Angela L.
Jill L.

Sandy L.
Sophie L.
Susan L.
Susan M.
Dwayne M.
Kenneth M.
Beverley M.
David M.
Fran M.
Michael M.
Laura M.
Mary Kay M.
Rachel M.
Donald M.
Kathleen M.
Kathleen M.
Marietsa M.
Kirk M.
Priscilla M.
Cynthia M.
Lisa M.
Margarita M.
JJ M.
JC M.
Melissa M.
Arthur M.
Terilynn M.
Eli M.
Genevieve M.
Beth M.
Glenn M.
Barbara M.
Natalie M.
Kerry M.
Joe M.
Pearse M.
Cheryl M.
Alyssa N.
Jean N.
Eleanor N.
Jessica K. N.
H. Ní A.
Amelia N.
Reilly N.
J. Michael N.
Helen N.
Diarmaid O C.
Ellen O'D.
David O'D.
Matt O.
Kelly O'R.
Beverly O.
K. W. O.
Mary P. C.
J. Ray P.
Brandon P.
Veronica P.
Jacob Paul P.
Hannah P.
Joan P.
Gustavo P. F.

Joseph P.
Karen P.
Steven P.
Tony P.
Lara P.
LeeAnn P.
Seth P.
S. J. P.
Stephen P.
Grant P.
Walker R.
Faizah R.
Helia R.
Bruce R.
Sin R.
Victoria R.
Peter R.
Bineta R.
Abby R.
Eric R.
Nataliya R.
Ellie R.
Laura Rose
AM R.
Gregory R.
Paul R.
Hana R.
Garrett R.
Claire R.
Michele R.
Angela R.
Michelle R.
Theodore R.
Michael S.
Imogen S.
Sameed S.
Glenn S.
Stephanie S.
Molly S.
Jonathan S.
Grace S.
Roberta S.
Kevin S.
Kathryn S.
Judith S.
Sandra S. H.
Solomon S.
Kathryn S.
John S.
David S.
Ernest S.
Mark S.
Howard S.
Morgan S.
Louise S.
Morgan S.
Madeline S.
Cameron S.
Harvey S.
Peggy Ann S.
Karen S.

Lisa St J.
Anna S.
Henry S.
Cally S. H.
Gregory S.
Margarite S.
Mark S.
Rachel S. J.
Andrew S.
Ellen S.
Shelley S.
M.K. S.
Leeny S.
Michael S.
Ron T.
Timothy T.
Donal T.
Nedda T.
Maureen T.
J. C. T.
Patricia T.
Terri T.
Sonya T.
Nicole T.
Meg T.
Michael T.
Ellen U.
Dianalee V.
Catherine V.
Pat W.
Robert W.
Carolyn W.
Michael W.
Michelle W.
Gail W.
Suellen W.
Ingrid W.
Mi W.
David W.
Linda W.
Laura W.
Charmaine W.
Jeanne W.
Lauren W.
JT W.
Guinotte W.
Juliet W.
Dan W.
Anne W.
Rob W.
Shannon Y.
Eleni Z.
Barbara Z.

THANK YOU

EDITOR-IN-CHIEF
Alexis Williams Carr

EDITOR EMERITUS
Don Williams

PUBLISHER
Brent Carr

MUSEPAPER *is an imprint of* NEW MILLENNIUM WRITINGS
and published with ♥ in Knoxville, Tennessee.

ISBN: 978-1-944977-12-2

MUSEPAPER BROADSIDES
View the ever-changing selection at musepaper.org/broadside.

SUBMISSIONS
For official rules and submission guidelines, please visit musepaper.org.

CONTACT
For volume discounts (writing groups/book clubs/educators), collaborations, and all other inquiries, the best method of contact is by email or through the websites.

Web: musepaper.org / newmillenniumwritings.com / sunshots.org
Em: hello@newmillenniumwritings.org
Ph: 646-798-6873

NEWMILLENNIUMWRITINGS.ORG | SUNSHOTS.ORG | MUSEPAPER.ORG

CONTENTS

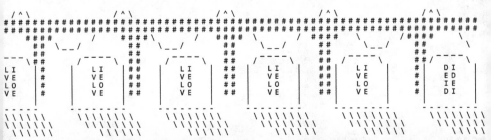

PRIZE WINNERS
MUSEPAPER 1.0

IN MEMORIAM

Apples
STORY PRIZE
Laura Maynard of Enniskillen, Ontario

Taking Our Time
ESSAY PRIZE
Jonathan Segol of Troy, NY

Ice Lessons
ESSAY PRIZE
M.K. Sturdevant of Chicago, Illinois

FINALISTS

H. Ní Aódagaín of Murphy, Oregon for "When Heroes Die"

Meredith Escudier of Oakland, California for "My Father's Eyes"

Nina Gaby of Brookfield, Vermont for
"Observations From the Girl Who Wasn't Even Under the Bridge"

Rowan Groth of Ewing, New Jersey for "Bye-Bye Johnny, Johnny Bye-Bye"

Carolyn Watkins of Taunton, Massachusetts for "The Born"

CHILDHOOD/PARENTHOOD

From the Garden
ESSAY PRIZE

Michele Flynn of Albany, New York

Folie Á Deux
ESSAY PRIZE

Laura Rose of Bucks County, Pennsylvania

Perfection
ESSAY PRIZE

Molly Seale of Makanda, Illinois

FINALISTS

Carrie Bailey of Vancouver, Washington for
"Open Letter To My Single Teenage Mother, a Career Waitress"

Diarmaid O Cuanain of Kildare, Ireland for "Revive"

Chris Guppy of Fort Collins, Colorado for "No Right To Be Wine"

Bruce Rettig of South Lake Tahoe, California for "Rabbit Hole"

Ellie Roscher of Minneapolis, Minnesota for "The Silence and the Cry"

MUSEPAPER PRIZE WINNERS

FRIENDSHIP

The One That Got Away
ESSAY PRIZE
Adrienne Garrison of Bloomington, Indiana

Jordan & Karyn
STORY PRIZE
Jude Brewer of Portland, Oregon

ICARUS
STORY PRIZE
Annie Dawid of Monument, Colorado

FINALISTS

H. Ní Aódagaín of Murphy, Oregon for "The Rituals of Love in Everyday Life"

John Barrale of Cliffside Park, New Jersey for "The Burden"

Maame Blue of Essex, United Kingdom for "A Cautious Friend"

Jessica Epstein of Atlanta, Georgia for "New Vocabulary"

S. J. Powers of Skokie, Illinois for "He Said, She Said"

FEAR

The Wolf In Me
POEM PRIZE
G.L. Connors of West Hartford, Connecticut

President Marilyn Monroe Devours Her Young
STORY PRIZE
Joanna Koch of Berkley, Michigan

Treats
STORY PRIZE
Brian Feehan of Wilton, Connecticut

FINALISTS

PS Cottier of Canberra, Australia for "Lax"

Myles Ehrlich of Brooklyn, New York for "Long Exposure"

Evelyn King of Craig, Colorado for "The Monsters Under My Bed"

Megan LeAnne of Nashville, Tennessee for "Habit"

Donald McCarthy of Levittown, New York for "First Date"

MUSIC

Tastes
ESSAY PRIZE

Kirk McDavitt of Bucharest, Romania

A Tale of Two Concerts
ESSAY PRIZE

Jeanne Wilkinson of Brooklyn, New York

Whatever Gets You Through the Night
POEM PRIZE

Sally Lipton Derringer of Nanuet, New York

FINALISTS

Melody Breyer-Grell of New York, New York for "Howling To Stan Getz"

Jessica Epstein of Atlanta, Georgia for "Fiddler's Neck"

Lori Levy of Sherman Oaks, California for "When I'm Old and Demented"

Dan Woessner of Sterling, Illinois for "The Lonely Hearts Club"

Rob Wright of Philadelphia, Pennsylvania for "Catching the Blues"

HOME

Advent Calendar
STORY PRIZE

Cezanne Alexander of Beaver, Washington

Little House
ESSAY PRIZE

Constance Campana of Norton, Massachusetts

SALT: A Homecoming
POEM PRIZE

Susan Maeder of the North Coast of California

FINALISTS

Susan Baller-Shepard of Bloomington, Illinois
for "Myra and the Clawed Frog"

Kelly Caldwell of New York, New York for "Perihelion"

Jennifer Lang of Raanana, Israel for "Neither Here Nor There"

Cynthia McVay of Ulster Park, New York for "Field Farm"

Jacob Paul Patchen of Cambridge, Ohio for "Where We Come From"

BEGINNINGS & ENDINGS

Ensō
ESSAY PRIZE

Natalie Mucker of Louisville, Kentucky

Expat
STORY PRIZE

Hana Rowan-Seddon of London, England

Beginnings
POEM PRIZE

Keith Mark Gaboury of San Francisco, California

FINALISTS

Jordan Crook of Issaquah, Washington for "The Flock"

Roberta Senechal de la Roche of Charlottesville, Virginia for "Bottle of Sleep"

Rachel Stewart Johnson of Poway, California for "Elegy for a Killdeer"

Seth Pilevsky of Woodmere, New York for "Not Ready"

S. J. Powers of Skokie, Illinois for "The News"

MUSEPAPER PRIZE WINNERS

REGRETS & RESOLUTIONS

The Cripple Makes a Wish
POEM PRIZE

Terri Trespicio of New York, New York

The Sum of its Parts
ESSAY PRIZE

Nina Gaby of Brookfield, Vermont

40
POEM PRIZE

Kathryn Gahl of Appleton, Wisconsin

FINALISTS

Kelli Bolen of Houston, Texas for "Aftermath"

Lois Engel of Washington, D.C. for "I Remember Mama"

Sandy Longley of Delmar, New York for "Pas de Deux"

JC Miller of Santa Rosa, California for "Monday, a Lament"

Claire Rubin of Oakland, California for "After What I Did"

LAURA MAYNARD

#

When babies die, people bring lasagna. They bring bread. They bring pie.

They arrive, single-file, wearing dark colors, with empty words and full hands, trying to lessen the void that hangs low in my belly.

"Thank you for coming," Daniel says. "She's not really eating much yet." He unclenches his fists to receive the plates.

He stuffs the casserole dishes into the freezer. Bits of snow chip off and fall to the floor. When the whispering voices cease and the front door closes, dishes smash against the walls.

There comes a time when Daniel stops throwing things and begins to cook. The scent of apple pie wafts upstairs and into the bedroom. My pillow is pungent and sour, desperation lingering in the yellow folds, but the aroma of the apples eclipses it momentarily. The sticky sweet triggers my memory of the orchard so long ago.

"Are you crazy? We can't do it here!" I'm laughing as Daniel pulls me down into a tall field beside the farthest row of apple trees. The grass bends easily beneath us, rejuvenated by the falling temperatures.

"Relax. There's no one around." He is hungry, watching the straps of my dress fall from my shoulders. "You can't be this beautiful and expect me to behave."

I hear the distant sounds of happy families filling their baskets at the east side of the orchard. His breath is hot in my ear and I have a good feeling about this one. Daniel is playful, laughing, grabbing at the fallen apples that dig into my back. Reflections of a baby shine in his eyes.

When I tell him that it's finally happened, he laughs. "It must have been the apples. They're magic."

The next day he brings home a tiny seedling and plants it in the backyard.

"You realize she'll be in college before that thing produces any fruit," I say. I've said "she" out loud for the first time, my hope slipping out, slamming the air.

He dismisses my sarcasm with a wave of his hand, spade over his shoulder. I smile at the kind of father he will be.

Now Daniel's weight on my side of the bed is familiar. "Please will you eat something?" He is gentle and pleading, dangling chunks of bread in front of me.

The smell is fresh and yeasty. As soon as she is born I press her bald head into my nose, drinking in the life we have created. I have just enough time to trace the tiny lines on her hands before they take her from me. She has my hands.

She is too quiet. My brain hovers between exhaustion and euphoria so that I barely notice when the doctor's face changes. It is the beeping of the machines that tips me off. And still, all of this is preferable to the silence that follows. The machines stop. Everybody stops.

The scent of the bread is in my nostrils and Daniel is still sitting on the bed. I push the bread away. It's wet. He doesn't even know he is crying.

After a tiny white casket has been lowered into the earth, people gather at my table to eat lasagna. I want to laugh and scream and claw my eyes out at the ridiculousness of this scene but, instead, I will my body to stay in the chair and obediently accept the food that is offered. The cheese stretches out only so far until it snaps, collapsing back down into the dish, smothered and low.

The people at the table examine my body openly. They give me the once over, trying not to let their eyes rest for too long on the loose flesh that hangs over top of a defective womb. Dark eyes. Hollow. They whisper, "When was the last time she ate?"

The mourners take away their empty platters so they can be filled again with the next sorrow. I munch on sedatives so that the blessing of oblivion will come. So that the people around me will stop their suicide watch. These offerings of food are well-meant, but they will not fill me up.

I am empty.

The doorbell rings less as the weeks go by. The house whispers and groans in the new silence and I have moved from the bed to the couch. My flesh has rearranged itself so that I no longer look like a woman who has just given birth. One less reminder. I am grateful for that at least.

There is a change in the air as the autumn wind rises, carrying colored leaves over top of naked trees. Wrapped in my blanket, I sit at the back window and watch Daniel rake the lawn. Leaves cling to his shirt, stick in his hair. He is surrounded by a halo of orange, red and gold. His shoulders are lower than I remember. He approaches the apple seedling, stopping in front to caress its tiny branches. The tree is small, but it has survived its first winter and is prepared to take on the next. Daniel uncoils the hose to water the tree. He wraps the skinny trunk in burlap, gentle hands smoothing every wrinkle. I begin to wonder if my memory has failed me. Perhaps she didn't have my hands after all; maybe they were more like Daniel's. Gazing at him, I am awed by his infinite capacity for hope.

He stops short when he enters through the back door to find me dressed and sitting at the kitchen table, eating a slice of pie. We stare at each other, and I see him for the first time in many weeks. He brushes at his eyes and walks over to the sink. His voice is tentative. "The tree is looking good," he says. "Once the roots get stable, it's not long before the apples come."

"Maybe by this time next year," I say.

Tears streaming down his face, he turns towards me just in time to see me smile. 🝔

JONATHAN SEGOL

TAKING OUR TIME

"Attention: it is now 11:30. The park will close at midnight. You have thirty minutes to leave the park."

The three of us — Roger, Billy, and me — could leave this park in two minutes, in any direction. It's a small neighborhood park. But after those instructions blare from the loudspeaker on the golfcart-sized vehicle with its headlight pointed at us, we agree it might take us longer leave to the park. Thirty-one minutes at least.

"Why leave the park at all?" Billy exclaims. "We should kick their asses. Remind them this curfew is bullshit."

"True enough," Roger answers, "though we'd get ours kicked much worse."

Roger got arrested the night the police ran everybody out of the park. Everybody — the punk band, their boisterous audience, the homeless encampment, and every random bystander. Roger was released without charges a few hours later, as were most people arrested there that day.

The next day, the city built a fence around the park as fast as anything gets built in this city. For renovations, they said. Park benches got more armrests so no one could sleep on them. The city removed the stage that the

5

band had played on (and Jimi Hendrix, Sonic Youth, and many others over the years). When the city reopened the park a few weeks ago, it was with a curfew. For a park that never had one, in a neighborhood full of night owls, many of us took it as a challenge.

"One rock," Billy continues. "One rock on the side of their golf cart. Just to remind them. A lucky shot could take out that floodlight they shined in our eyes."

We go back and forth on this question for too much of the next half hour. We've got a guitar; we should be sharing songs right now. Roger's are great, like a punk Woody Guthrie. Mine are a mess but I want him to hear some. Billy plays with a band. He would have an album out by now, but the producers who were interested got scared off for the same reason we love his shows: every moment's a surprise. He might switch songs halfway through, start shouting at a passerby, or even try to climb a wall. Which should make me nervous when he talks about throwing a rock.

"You could throw it," Roger answers, "but they've got spare headlights at the precinct on the next block, right? Golf carts too." This is how Roger calms Billy down. Concedes he can do anything anytime and envisions nothing changing from it. Billy sounds a wordless grumble to suggest he'll think about it.

11:55 and the loudspeakers repeat. The golf cart's headlight keeps returning to us, since we are among the last people in the park. It's so bright that I can't tell how many people are riding it toward us. We walk but we take it slow. No one can say we are not leaving. As we approach the park entrance, ten cops on each side of us tell us to get a move on, their voices a mix of calm and commanding. If I were older I might feel for the cops—how they've been assigned to change this neighborhood into a place they can't afford to live. I might ask them to give us more space, to reassure them that we're leaving and we need not argue as to whether it is 11:59 or 12:01.

Billy does have a rock in his jacket, a good size to throw. But even Billy knows we can't stop the neighborhood's rent from quadrupling, scattering us past the park to other boroughs, upstate and points beyond, as the city finally repairs these streets for its new residents. All we can do is move slow, nonchalant but tough, and steal back this crumb of time, one minute after midnight. ⬡

M.K. STURDEVANT

ICE LESSONS

I'm running next to the lake, leaping and punching through the fog. It's spring, freezing cold. Heart pounding, I gasp it, I spit it out once more, to let him know that now is a good time. There's nobody around. *Now, Dad. Come now!* There are merely millions of shadows, flickers in high-rise windows to the west. I pause on my path, and not even a gull flaps. I can only hear the lake breaking, shifting ice all around, and I hear the plates rolling, slicing, and shattering little by little: his steady crackle. He is the line being drawn from here to Benton Harbor, a noise drawn deep under Sister Bay, a shift in the light over Milwaukee.

I'm walking home later, trying to figure out what he was up to, what he wanted to say. I worry I didn't get the message.

Dad and I go grocery shopping sometimes. He's so funny about cereal. He mixes up about four different kinds in his bowl. So I ask him, *Dad, which kind should I get?* I see his favorite brand, and I buy it. At breakfast, I eat a bowl of that, mixed with a few other things. I add fruit. I have this smug look on my face because he's

8

going to tell this joke about the cost of raspberries. He grew his own in his backyard in Cortez, but he can't sell them since it's against some code to sell things that grew where you buried your dog. *They taste the same!* he insists. I laugh so hard, and my husband is pissed because what is so funny on a Tuesday at 7:15 a.m. when we're in a hurry and there's no one eating but me.

He came to my birthday last month. I was home out west. I was up in the mountains. I was talking to him in my head all day, *Dad this, Dad that, Dad try to come to my party somehow and I'll have Michael sing Jingle Bells for you.* He always does the best he can. Mom had her internet radio on, and there's no reason it would play Sixteen Candles, but it did. I'm much older now, but it was ours: *Happy Birthday Baby oh, I love you so.* I stood by her desk and listened to the computer weaving us, coding the warp, signaling weft, deathless.

That night, I laid down next to my husband. We began doing our usual audit of things that need doing—did you turn off the fireplace, did you plug in your phone, did you give Michael his paci—when we quieted for a moment wondering at how dark it is in these woods. Even in the fullness of air so black, there was a moon and it made the thin lace curtains blue. Against the blue-mooned curtains a shadow suddenly arced. Our hearts popped and we waited for what to do, when the intruder took another step forward and we saw his three-point rack. Oh god, okay, my husband said. The mid-sized buck breathed some frost at the glass and checked on us, confirmed we were alright, and pointed his rack downslope again. Then he looked back, all the weight of his crown following. *Thanks,* I smiled.

He watches me all the time now, even here in this sharp, tall city, in the last city he was ever in because he came to visit me and he got stuck here, in a way. He knows his way around; he knows where I park. He told me the other day in a slap of wind to turn around because I left the rear window down. *Someone could break in.* Yeah yeah, *and if my head weren't screwed on, et cetera, I know,* I said.

I was headed into the office at the time. I took a can of Folgers into the break-room. They all looked at me. They're all in the know about coffee-roasting, I guess. Well, I drink Folgers now. I study it when I drink it. I want to know everything about it. *See, Dad? Come have your coffee.* And so he'll try to have a cup with me, or I'll become him; I'll even chew up some Tums with the coffee and see what it was like to be him. My eyes are hot. The door is wide open. I hope he isn't scared. *I'm not scared Dad, come on, come in, I have your mouth now.*

He's on his way. I don't weep. The point at which my eyes heat up—when I remember the neurotrauma surgeon calling out his name, and asking him to squeeze his pen, which Dad did not—I bite down and become stone. He has other ways.

I might never go ice-fishing on Groundhog Reservoir again. I couldn't drill down with the augur as well as my brothers. I laughed, inside my parka, watching them do it.

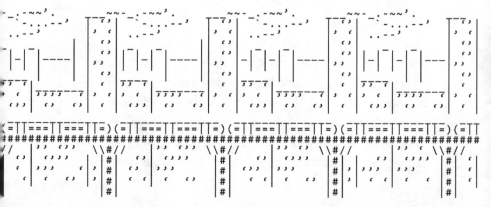

Ice can be like marble, like glass. It can have gray, ivory, and bright blackness in it. It makes a noise: *pull the augur at this angle, drop your line quietly here. Sit.*

The fish my dad pulled up hours later was pure muscle, pure life, and we soaked it in lemon and ate it. Around the same table and same lamp as always, in a room that I kept promising to belong to again, we bit into the fish and shook flecks of dill onto it. We became sustained by the fish who was fed by the lake, and I knew the only promise I could ever make was that I would believe neither in an afterlife, nor in finitude.

I only know for certain, I tell him, standing at the edge, hearing the marbled snore of a lake turning over, *that we are teeming with elemental presence. Dad, we're heavy with an infinitude of variations.* We've always been something, somewhere.

I taught you that, he says. 🜂

MICHELE FLYNN

FROM THE GARDEN

We live in a small city and tend a shady backyard the size of two Ford Explorers. Half of the yard is covered in paving stones, and the other half is grass. We buy sod each year, roll it out and water it. It lasts through mid-September and inexplicably dies. My five-year-old thinks that grass is an annual that comes in rolls like toilet paper. But he also knows that peas come in pods and potatoes must be dug out of the ground. At least once a week, I pull our tools and Jake in a red radio flyer wagon to a sunny community garden plot one block from home. We don't grow prize-winning tea roses. We play in the dirt, and bury seeds, wait for them to sprout, and ask questions: "Will it grow to the sky like in Jack and the Beanstalk?" "Will it be red?" and most importantly, "How does it taste?"

Jake and I live a parallel life in the garden, one with more wonder and less stress. The short trip in the wagon brings us miles away from our normal lives. The same mommy who screeches at him to put on clean clothes for school, smiles and shakes her head as he wades in mud past his ankles, even if he's wearing new sneakers.

Musepaper Essay Prize, Volume 1, 2019
'From The Garden' © 2017 Michele Flynn

I'm sure he prefers his Garden Mommy.

The gardener with the plot next to ours told us that it's tradition to plant peas on St. Patrick's Day. Jake never questions this, even though some years we've cleared away snow to sow our seeds. Instead he pushes chubby handfuls of peas into the earth, while I carefully space them as per seed package directions. His always come up. Mine don't. We've found that gardening is an art, not a science, and that we get along better with fewer rules.

With dirt, bricks, sticks, and stakes, Jake builds hide-outs for his superheroes, castles for his knights, and burrows for his new earthworm friends. At home he wants me in his sight, and preferably within his reach. In the garden, he shovels contentedly and isn't aware of where I am.

Last spring, Jake's pet crab died. Since I felt more comfortable talking about death in the garden where we've watched plants sprout, grow, bloom, and die, we decided to give Crabby a suitable and convenient burial beneath our planned sunflower house. In preparation, Jake drew a memorial picture of Crabby. We carried the dead crustacean to the garden and dug a deep hole, so no one would be tempted, or able, to dig her up. Jake wasn't interested in covering her with dirt, so I shoveled. As we planted the seeds, I explained that Crabby's body would help the flowers grow. Fast forward to the fall. We pulled up the dead tree-like sunflower stalks to prepare the garden for winter, breaking one apart to look at the mysterious cross-section of stem. Jake said, "Crabby must be in there." I had forgotten about Crabby's burial. Jake hadn't. What's more, he probably hadn't forgotten that his best friend's mother had also died that spring.

As frost threatens and the harvest slowly ends, we're sad. Jake doesn't believe that we can't keep growing things.

After all, we planted peas under the snow. He expects strawberries in October, and cucumbers in November.

Last Christmas Eve, Jake and I dug potatoes for Christmas dinner. How I coerced him, on the very same day Santa was to arrive, I don't know. I remember that it took a lot of threatening about elves watching. Kneeling in the potato patch, we fell onto all fours and dug like dogs, dirt flying through our legs, until we found potatoes.

Each season we grow with our plants and our knowledge of each other. In the garden, Jake carefully shares his thoughts and I have time to listen. Time momentarily sits still. We suspend the rules, relax, and are allowed be ourselves. We feel breezes, sunshine, and sometimes rain. It's not the mall. There's nothing to buy. It's not the Multiplex. There's no admission. It's not TV. There are no commercials. My kid gets to be a kid. I get to be a mom.

This year, my younger son Matty, who is not yet two, planted peas in the cold March dirt. His seedlings came up alongside Jake's. I didn't plant peas this year. Instead, I sat at the feet of the masters and took notes.

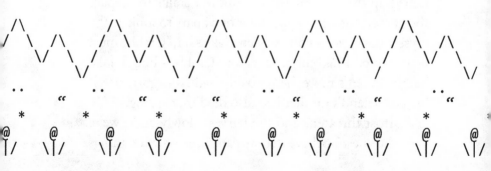

LAURA ROSE

FOLIE À DEUX

It's a still, sweet July evening. The air is cool, the sky cloudless. The birds are chattering away in the hedgerow outside of our cabin where my family spends the summer. We're isolated from the world. Mile after square mile of dense Pennsylvania forest stretches out beyond the hedgerow, a four-mile dirt road separates us from the nearest town. My father is on the front porch staring into the woods. I watch him through the kitchen window.

I'm twelve years old and my parents' marriage is on life support. The air is thick with silence. Each glance my father throws at my mother slams into her body, making her limp and weepy. The rest of the time she's hard like marble. I go to hug her and she recoils. "Stop hanging on me," she says. "You're not a monkey."

My father is different. He's gone inside of himself, inside of his own head, and only emerges in her absence. Just yesterday he asked me to take a boat ride. It was odd because he never took me anywhere by myself, but I said sure. The lake was like a mirror, and iridescent green and purple dragonflies swirled above our heads. After we'd rowed to the middle and made small conversation about the sunset, he unburdened himself about their marriage. How unhappy he was, how crazy my mother was, how she was sick and would always be sick, and how he couldn't live this way forever. I put my hand in the water and let it flow through my parted fingers, and I pushed his voice away until it was nothing but a heavy, dead hum. He talked and I said yes and no in all the right places, even as I threw a piece of my soul into the water for the perch to feed on.

And now I'm back from a day of swimming. Dinner is on its way and I set the table for my mother. It makes her happy when I do something without her having to ask, and I want her to be happy. As I set the table, I watch my father through the window. He's on the porch facing the woods, his arms in front of him as if he's holding something. There's something about the way his arms are bent and how he stares at the woods that is both frightening and compelling. My head starts to buzz. It's the buzzing that always starts as I'm drawn to danger — like when my brother set off those M-80s with his friend in the woods — and soon the ping pong balls get going in my chest. Then like some moron in a horror movie, I move toward the thing that terrifies me. I open the screen door, and step onto the porch, and move close enough to my father to see him holding his .22-caliber rifle. The stock is dark and smooth and polished, the barrel spotless. He turns to me, and he has the bad eyes. The hard, wild eyes that both see you and don't. I look at the gun and ask him if he's going to shoot skeet. I know he's not, but it's better than asking him what he's doing because he might take it the wrong way.

"Hear them?" he asks.

"Hear what?"

"The dogs."

I can't hear anything because my heart is beating in my ears and the ping-pong balls are knocking around in my chest.

"There's a pack of dogs out there." He cocks his head. "You hear?"

I hear birds singing in the hedgerow and blood whooshing in my ears, but the dogs may be very far away, and my father has better ears than me.

"Where would they come from?"

"Sometimes farmers' dogs get loose and run away. They turn wild and form a pack." I must look scared because he lifts up his rifle and says, "Don't worry. I'm ready."

I will my ears into becoming superhuman like my father's, like a barn owl's, like the Bionic Woman's. And then I do hear something. Maybe it's the faint yaps of dogs carried on the wind, maybe it's the movement of air and blood in my ears. There's my father, the gun, his bad eyes. I need to hear something.

"Mom needs help with dinner," I say. Then I go to my room, sit on my bed, and push the fear down until it's nothing but a heavy, dead hum.

It's a quiet night, ten years later. I'm reading a chapter for my Abnormal Psychology class and come across the phrase, *folie á deux*. It's French for *the madness of two*. It's when one person suffers from a delusion—like their dental fillings are receiving radio signals—and another person gets drawn into believing it herself. I close the book and wonder how anyone could be so suggestible, so gullible, so fucking stupid, then turn in for the night.

I pop up in bed like a funhouse dummy two hours later, wet sheets sticking to my chest. Still panting, I gather the pieces of my nightmare before it dissolves. I'm walking alone in the woods when I see a grizzly bear sitting on its filthy haunches. He's going to tear me to pieces. Then five more appear. I don't dare run. Running will only provoke them.

I get up and change my shirt. As I crawl back into bed, I think, *folie á deux*, and then in a flash I see my father on the porch holding his gun.

You are twelve years old. It's a still, sweet July evening. The air is cool, the sky cloudless. Your father is on the front porch, rifle in hand, staring into the woods with his bad eyes. Can you hear the dogs? Do you want to hear them more than anything you've wanted in your entire life? 🔹

MOLLY SEALE

PERFECTION

My aunt sits across from me. I have settled in the one rocking chair in her home and my eighteen-month-old toddler is climbing onto my lap. "Nurse, Mommy! Nurse!" he demands. He's weary, always so after a car trip. His eyes are heavy, he longs for the comfort of my breast. "Do you mind?" I ask. "Oh, not at all," she smiles as I lift my shirt and he, my baby, latches on greedily, sleepily, gratefully.

My aunt — Golda is her name — smiles gently, watching me, watching him. She is silky and soft, fragrant and old, so old. Yet she curiously observes the two of us and I venture, "What was your son like at this age? Do you remember him then?"

She lights up. Truly, like a lamp switched on, she is aglow as she recounts how he nursed, how he slept through the night early on, how he was forever cheerful, never fussy. No, not ever. What a delight he had been to her, to his father. What an absolute joy.

I remember him, her son, my cousin. He died five years previously, and although I'd heard of him my entire life, I'd met him only a few years before his death. At that time he was in his early fifties, thirty years older than me,

19

and he had returned home to help his mother run the country store after his father died. My young husband and I, freshly married, stopped in at the store expecting to surprise my aunt. But she wasn't there. Instead, he was there. Or at least I figured he was my cousin, for who else could he be? I explained who I was, how we were related, and he struggled to understand. As I repeated my parents' names, "Jim and Lucile. I am Jim and Lucile's daughter," he finally remembered, or pretended to. "Oh yes, them!" he mumbled, and vaguely smiled. He attempted to speak, but he could not quite form a sentence. In silence, I purchased a pack of gum, gave him a dollar, watched uncomfortably as he strained to make change. Indeed, he couldn't. We left with weak good-byes. "Tell Aunt Golda we were here. So happy to have met you at last!" He nodded, tried again to smile.

Aunt Golda was sixteen years old when she gave birth to her only son, a beauty of a baby, a charmer from the moment of his birth. My parents knew him as a gleaming, exquisite, joyous child, full of cheer, sweet deeds, good intentions. And brilliant. Oh yes, a brilliant little boy who adored all, was adored by all. They knew him too as a brave young man — off to war at eighteen years of age. And they knew him as a returning World War II hero, wildly decorated, including with the Purple Heart. He had survived the Battle of the Bulge and met up with a gorgeous French woman, fifteen years older, who he brought home on his perfect, uniformed arm. The kinfolk, the neighbors, the entire little town now not only adored him, they revered him. They were skeptical, however, of his wife, Monique, whose name they pronounced 'Monick' in their heavy Texan drawls.

After his return, he sold cars, then insurance. He and Monique moved to another town, a larger one where prying eyes and nagging tongues did not judge him for his choice of a spouse. They had a child, but after many years they divorced. This was a great tragedy in our extended family, as husbands and wives simply did not divorce, even when the men were, in the words of my father, "drunks, womanizers, no goods." Which, in fact, my cousin had become.

No one understood what happened to him. Why he married that 'foreign' woman. Why he moved away to Beaumont instead of staying near home. Why he cheated on his wife. Why he lost job after job. Why he drank and drank and drank. Why he died of cirrhosis.

But on this day, in my aunt's tidy home, my son satiated and dozing in my arms — so new and fresh and lovely and loved — we do not speak of her son's hard life, of the war that sent him home physically intact but mentally and emotionally battered. We do not speak of the few years before his death, when he lived in this house with her and she experienced the loss of a son still living, the heartbreak of a son dying a debilitating, painful death.

We do not speak of his transformation, how the awards for bravery in battle took away his freshness, robbed him of all joy. We do not speak of how young he was and how, sensing his youth, his bright future, he brought home a wife, fathered a child, and tried to support them. And in the end, when he seemed beyond hope, he returned to his mother, to help her, he insisted, in her old age.

As my son sleeps in my arms, what strikes me is that my aunt has not given up on her son. No matter that he suffered, ruined the lives of others, relinquished responsibility to those he loved and who loved him. No matter. She remembers his baby smell, his wide eyes gazing up at her as he fed, his pealing laughter and softness, cleanliness. His tender touch. His breath.

No matter. He was her perfection. And even now, more than sixty years later, the wreck he became buried five years before, he remains so, her purest gift, her precious one, her most beloved.

And I know, I am certain, that I will be the same. Regardless of what lies before me, before my son, I will return to this fresh moment, this golden sharing as I sit with my aunt who smiles wistfully as she tells me of her perfect baby boy, as I cradle my own cherished one in my arms, firm and steady and safe. 🔷

ADRIENNE GARRISON

The One That
Got Away

I woke up out of a dead sleep thinking of her.

If I'm honest, I was dreaming about her. What was the dream? It doesn't matter.

I woke up out of a dead sleep, heartbroken.

The one that got away was my best friend. I remember the day that she asked me, after Sunday school in the fifth grade, if I could spend the night at her house sometime.

And at her house in seventh grade, getting ready for a football game, our cheer outfits wrapped around our small, self-conscious bodies, eyes glittering with excitement and, well—it was the late 90's, so—actual glitter.

I remember in eighth grade when I sort of went out with a boy that she liked and she wrote me a note asking me not to. I laughed, felt cheated for a microsecond, but suddenly found that he no longer interested me.

Sometimes we saw a lot of each other. Other times, for reasons only partially dictated by geography, she was surrounded with friends and activities in her life in town and I was alone a lot, excluded a lot, in my life in the country.

But year after year, our friendship persevered. Through impossibly tricky teenage years, dating drama, parental tension, college, pregnancy, and marriage. We stood up in each other's weddings, and for months before each one, we showed up for each other: picking out accessories, planning hairstyles, researching venues, carefully writing out place cards.

Best friends to bridesmaids. At that point, we'd officially grown up together, cemented our nearly lifelong bond of being there for one another, through anything. Even as careers, family, and distance made our connection more complicated and less frequent, we found a way to be there for one another. Laughing, remembering.

That's why, about a year later, when she stopped returning my calls, I knew I must have done something wrong.

The weeks and months that passed after texts and calls went unanswered left plenty of time for me to lie in bed at night sifting through memories, trying to find the key to what went wrong. Eventually, I found it. The small but significant piece of information that I had shared with someone else. The betrayal.

24

I held it up to the light, nearly a year after I'd last spoken to my friend, and understood that the friendship

```
ove You!        I Love You!          I Love You!          I Love You!
       I Love You           I Love You           I Love You
Bb.d88b,I Love ,d88b.d88b, I Love,d88b.d88b,u I Lov,d88b.d88b,ou I
88888888 You I 88888888888e You I88888888888ve You 88888888888ove
888888Y'Love Yo`Y8888888Y' Love Y`Y8888888Y'I Love `Y8888888Y' I L
Y888Y'You I Love `Y888Y' You I Love`Y888Y'e You I Lov`Y888Y've You
v`Y'I Love You I Lo`Y' I Love You I L`Y'u I Love You I `Y'ou I Lov
I Love You        I Love You          I Love You          I Love Yo
       I Love You           I Love You           I Love You
ove You!        I Love You!          I Love You!          I Love You!
       I Love You           I Love You           I Love You
Bb.d88b,I Love ,d88b.d88b, I Love,d88b.d88b,u I Lov,d88b.d88b,ou I
88888888 You I 88888888888e You I88888888888ve You 88888888888ove
888888Y'Love Yo`Y8888888Y' Love Y`Y8888888Y'I Love `Y8888888Y' I L
Y888Y'You I Love `Y888Y' You I Love`Y888Y'e You I Lov`Y888Y've You
J`Y'I Love You I Lo`Y' I Love You I L`Y'u I Love You I `Y'ou I Love
```

was over. I understood that she couldn't move past it, and now, with me living across the country, why should she bother? The late-night brownies, the hours spent getting ready together, the secret jokes and hysterical laughter—they just didn't matter, didn't stack up to how I had failed her. That is what I was forced to conclude from the empty space between each of my "how are you? miss you" texts.

So the part of me that had fought fiercely for that friendship for fifteen years laid down inside my heart. Gave up. Surrendered. The friendship was already lost. When circumstance blew news of her life through the corridors of my awareness, that part of me lifted its head a bit to see the picture of her daughter on social media, looking exactly like her. And months later, that part of me ached to show her the tiny bundle of pink in my own arms, that in a few months would seem to look exactly like me.

Five years have passed this way, since my friend-for-life gave me up and got on with her own life. I understood it. I accepted it. What could I do? We were such different people now anyway.

But last night I woke up from a deep sleep, memories of her face and her voice still hanging in my mind like a dream fog, and my heart immediately focused on this one truth: I had to try. The part of me that had loved her

```
Love You!        I Love You!          I Love You!          I Love You!
           I Love You            I Love You            I Love You
88b.d88b,I Love ,d88b.d88b, I Love,d88b.d88b,u I Lov,d88b.d88b,ou I
388888888 You I 88888888888e You I88888888888ve You 88888888888ove
3888888Y'Love Yo`Y8888888Y' Love Y`Y8888888Y'I Love `Y8888888Y' I  }
`Y888Y'You I Love `Y888Y' You I Love`Y888Y'e You I Lov`Y888Y've Yo
ɔv`Y'I Love You I Lo`Y' I Love You I L`Y'u I Love You I `Y'ou I Lo
  I Love You           I Love You           I Love You           I Love Ye
ij           I Love You            I Love You            I Love You
Love You!        I Love You!          I Love You!          I Love You!
ij           I Love You            I Love You            I Love You
88b.d88b,I Love ,d88b.d88b, I Love,d88b.d88b,u I Lov,d88b.d88b,ou
388888888 You I 88888888888e You I88888888888ve You 88888888888ove
3888888Y'Love Yo`Y8888888Y' Love Y`Y8888888Y'I Love `Y8888888Y' I
`Y888Y'You I Love `Y888Y' You I Love`Y888Y'e You I Lov`Y888Y've Yo
ɔv`Y'I Love You I Lo`Y' I Love You I L`Y'u I Love You I `Y'ou I Lo
```

so fiercely as a friend, and who had laid down wrapped in a white flag of surrender, stood up. It took up both fists and banged on the wall of my heart, crying "You must ask her. You must."

And I knew it was right. I must ask her. For forgiveness.

I typed out these words as I waited for the sun to rise, steeling myself that this might be another message sent and unanswered. That this might not be enough to heal what was broken. That she might actually answer, that she might actually forgive. Sparks of fear leapt up from all of these possibilities until, when the hour became decent, I called. 🜲

Jordan & Karyn

My friend Jordan spreads almond butter on his bananas. Peel, spread, bite, chew. He talks between swallowing and spreading.

"My world view is fucked," he says.

My friend Karyn switches one hat off the rack for another.

"That's more rivery-hatty," she says.

Jordan calls daily until he starts calling monthly, and I wonder if it's the turning point of our friendship where we've forgotten our lives outside of our routines.

Karyn helps me pick out a new pair of frames for my prescription glasses. I wonder if it's the turning point of our relationship, the downfall, so to speak, since she's fonder of them than I am. I wonder if maybe she doesn't want me looking too attractive.

Jordan reveals he's started a podcast around the same time I've started a podcast, and we're listening to both and saying we're proud of the other and we like how it sounds, but I wonder, fleetingly, if we're being honest. I know I am, but is he? And is he wondering the same? I'm wondering how to express pride for him without expressing too much, without appearing too eager or too wrapped up in the minutia of the conversations we used to have when I didn't analyze how they went for hours afterward.

Karyn writes a song about our cats, but it could be mistaken for a song about a cranky old couple, which is exactly what she wanted, but some of her lyrical choices are not my favorite and I want to tell her that but I don't because I never have before, so why would I start telling her now?

A crowd is divided in half, split down the center where I walk toward Jordan. Then Karyn walks toward us. He says to us and to the crowd, "Love is an action, not a feeling." He says this, among other things, before asking us to read what we've written down, before we exchange rings. Karyn cries, and I can no longer count how many times she's cried with me on just two hands; now I'll need ten fingers and a toe.

Karyn is three time zones over on tour playing music for strangers, and Jordan is a time zone over jamming on the guitar with old friends in his basement, and I'm listening to classical music for a change, and the television is off, and I'm ignoring whatever notifications pop up on my smartphone, and my tea has grown cold, the gingerbread flavor stiff, but I'm still sipping away and listening for the rain they've promised us.

Jordan texts me:

> *If life/perception is on a continuum of nihilism and its opposite (i.e., everything fucking matters), then living life accordingly to one or the other will certainly yield very different outcomes. It's truly unknowable… whether this all matters…or whether we're all just bacteria floating through space on some giant alien's galactic turd.*

Karyn texts me:

> *I wonder what our farts will smell like when we are old?* 🎲

ANNIE DAWID

ICARUS

The hostess had drawn a simple scene on the mirror, using crank and a razor for paint and brush. She drew a mountain range and the sun setting into the sea—an ocean of speed. Crystalline powder curved in a near-perfect circle to make the sun and jutted at precipitous angles to form the jagged peaks of a ridge. You called me over to see.

"After you."

I eliminated the horizon. You made the sun disappear. The white granules flew neatly up the straw, defying gravity.

The party swirled around us in primary colors: bright yellow clothing on red Mediterranean skin, and the rich blue of lapis shimmering from necks and wrists and ears. The Portuguese had eyes like the centers of sunflowers: infinitely brown, pupils hidden like seeds. Your eyes were turquoise like the sea.

I stretched my legs to rest them on the tip of your chair. You clasped an ankle and ran your fingertips down the arch of my foot. Someone was playing saxophone; music and voices bounced off walls, collided in corners, volume swelling until it exploded in laughter and scat-sung wails.

Musepaper Story Prize, Volume 1, 2019
'Icarus' © 2017 Annie Dawid

The hostess reappeared, flourishing a tray. On it were a dozen goblets of champagne, liquid hissing. She smiled at us, carmine lips uncovering fluorescent teeth.

We each accepted a glass, mouthing our thank-yous with exaggerated vowels. She smiled again, then receded into the din of conversation and color.

I felt my heart racing against my brain, pulse accelerating when you leaned to whisper, "Let's disappear."

I shut the door on noise but the hostess's trill of laughter escaped in a helix and followed us out into the night. The peninsula stretched flat ahead; only the shadows of cactus intervened between the party behind us and the lighthouse that marked the western extremity of Europe.

At the tip of Portugal, one can go no farther. Centuries before, the most daring explorers believed this promontory was the end of the world and named it *Fim do Mundo*. By sailing beyond the horizon, one would drop off the edge of existence.

You ran down a cliffside path where the only sound was the slapping of the sea on boulders a hundred feet below. I removed my shoes and started after you. I saw you standing still on a rock beside the edge, your head tilted back, mouth and eyes open wide: the meteorite shower.

Millions of stars glittered in the blackness, and every sixty seconds the beacon from the lighthouse flashed illumination upon the sea and sand in a sweeping arc. Looking straight up, we could sense those stars that fell, violently, beyond our vision. Entire constellations took their gleam from the hidden sun and showered the water with fireworks.

"I wish I could see more," I said, wanting to see all, to see every fleck of light as it danced downward and out of sight.

You lifted me by the waist and then held my knees to your chest; I was a particle in the black-and-white kaleidoscope of the sky.

Cool air vibrated against my lips. For one moment I believed that I was detached from the earth and its rules. When you set me down, I stumbled—still reeling with the stars—and you caught me before I hit the ground.

We knelt at the edge of the world, suspended above the water and in the center of the meteorite shower. The dying stars rained light upon us, setting fire to our methamphetamine wings; I thought nothing could ever be ordinary again.

You kissed the hollow by my collarbone, trailed your lips up the back of my neck. We lay on granite rocks, watching the cascade of ancient suns. I heard a whistle, a barely perceptible hiss, and turned in the direction of the sound.

An orange disk streaked a path above the horizon, outshining all other meteors, leaving a train of embers in its wake before falling into the sea.

"Remember Icarus?" I asked.

You said, "That might be him, never us."

PRESIDENT MARILYN MONROE DEVOURS HER YOUNG

I'm going to disappoint you. But you know that already.
If I don't, you'll keep me around and alive. And where
will that leave us? Like an old married couple. Like a
husband and wife.

I know why you're here. You've heard the rumors. You
want to see for yourself, take a short dip in the glory hole.
Pardon my obscene, anachronistic cliché. I'm a bit of an
obscene anachronism myself. You've peeped night after
night, and now you're inside. Tell me, baby, is it everything
you dreamed? All you desired? You think you like it, but
get to know me better. You won't.

No one ever likes it as much as they want it.

I built this empire on making promises, not keeping
them. Glamour is a veil. The bride loses power when she
lifts the mask. Mystery keeps customers coming back. It's
the same in politics as in burlesque: a girl's got to save
something for the last act. Trust me, underneath this

chemise, I'm no different than all the monsters who've ruled the world. Under every suit lurks an identical shadow.

I promise I won't fight. You might as well untie these silly knots. My muscle tone is surgically sculpted for visual effect, not strength. The camera adores my implants. Feel how soft and pliant they are. See, doesn't that feel nice?

Ah, that's better. I'd rather get in on the fun than be a spectator at my own rape. You knew that, didn't you, when you dragged me here. You ripped the silk curtains, snarled at the roses, and kicked over the vanity. What a brute! No alarm sounded; no guard stood sentry as you seized me. Your High Priestess was like a call girl waiting on a buck. And now you ask: Where is the power? Where is the glory?

I ask of you, my child: Where is the kingdom? In this country, this building, this room? Is it a fortress keeping us apart? A selective membrane of history binding us together? If the kingdom of heaven dwells not within you or me, it dwells not at all. In times like this and for creatures like us, there is only the kingdom of hell.

Don't look like that, baby. A girl can have a laugh, especially when she's facing the end. That pistol is such a bad prop. Exactly what the audience expects. Shall we give them a twist? Put it down. Give me a sporting chance.

The audience? But of course there's an audience. There's always an audience!

The office of High Priestess demands a non-stop global performance. We strive for a climax every six to eight hours to saturate international time zones. My circadian rhythms are chemically amped. It's such a high. Makes a girl ravenous, though. It's a miracle I can maintain my figure.

Congratulations, baby. Privacy is a relic of the past. Every centimeter of the Pink House is wired for surveillance and simulcast. It's been a slow news day. You're the new star! The audience is jaded, impatient with the dance of veils and hungry for the dance of death. I can bring twenty thugs rushing in to break your body down into donation-quality organs by batting an eyelash. I can roast you like a fatted calf. Once the audience gets hungry, they aren't too picky about the dish.

But I'm not like that, baby. I forgive you. I forgive everything. That's what goddesses do.

Come close. Now I can see you. I want you. Ignore the chant of the crowd, the mewling of one thousand hungry young. I told you there was an audience. Stop teasing. I want you. Who cares if the sound is closer? It is merely a sound. It is the rhythm of a slathering mob, infantile and insatiable. Their cries pound apart the soft walls of reason. Their screams suckle upon their own echo, opening void upon void. You hear yourself in that sound, for it is sworn of ceaseless agony, sick with desire.

Enter me, yes, like that. Unleash your rage for all I've promised, yes, don't stop. Wallow among the horde, in my kingdom, consumed. You're the brute, the star, the baby I'm taking back. You'll want me forever, but you'll never have me. I'm nothing, the shadow in every suit, the sacrament that swallows the host. You dwell in me forever. I am ageless, mindless, and desired by all. There is no end to desire in the kingdom of heaven.

BRIAN FEEHAN

TREATS

Elliott is delighted with the selections, albeit a bit over-whelmed. So many choices, so many alternatives, so many decisions that have to be made: combos or solos, super-sized or regular, sodas or shakes or some sweetened tea? And then the toys. Which to choose to complete the meal? The girls, he assumes, would love the princess action figurines (he has a choice of six). A special treat on their special day. But what about the wee one? Mightn't he like a truck or soldier or…whatever that is? The colors and the smells and the bright smiling faces are almost too much for Elliot to bear and he begins to breathe, in that way that he does.

The little girl in front of him turns towards Elliot. (*He mustn't he mustn't he…*) She is dressed as a kitten, bewhiskered and black (*pussycat, pussycat I love…*) but then she is back clutching onto mommy, or so Elliot assumes, resuming her fidget and insistent whine. Elliott would not allow such behavior. If the little girl were his (if the little girl were *his*), she would not stare at strange men or fidget or whine. She would stand stock-still, completely composed, holding onto his hand till their turn had come.

36

Their turn.

Other ghouls and goblins are waiting in line. Any might come to his doorstep tonight, with a knock or a bell and a bag full of... Elliot has choices to make. He doesn't want to arrive at the gleaming counter, below bright shiny boards filled with pictures and numbers, with decisions unmade; doesn't want to be one of 'those' that get to the front only to stare and to mumble as if the simplest of choices were overwhelming to them (*he mustn't he mustn't he*).

The little pussycat (Elliot has named her 'Margaret') wants a shake—a 'nilla' one, is insisting on it. Margaret should not be allowed to have milkshakes, not with this type of behavior. Not a 'nilla', or strumberry or that odd shade of ginger that is called 'pumpkin spice'. Margaret needs discipline, it is painfully clear to him. If Margaret were his and she had acted this way, when they had gotten to the front he would encourage her to speak to the smiling clerk, "speak nice and clearly, that's a good girl", and when she had completed her task, he would tell the clerk (smiling Bobby or Bill) to cancel her order—tell him that Margaret had not been a good girl, not an exemplary example of how a little princess should act. No meals for her, happy or otherwise. He would ask smiling Billy or Bob to cancel her order. Then he would place his own and she would sit across from Elliott and watch as he ate, savoring each morsel—every humdinger bit. But Margaret cannot be his concern. Margaret is doomed to go through life clutched to this woman with no parenting skills. *(You need a license to have a dog, but any bitch can give birth.)* There should be a law or a court or a governing body with applications and tests and courses to complete. Elliot could teach such a class. Elliott could run the whole god-damned she-bang.

She is staring again. Margaret. Elliott feels the itch—the palm of his left hand, the back of his knee. He can't start scratching or the others might notice. They might whisper to the manager or give him a nod and he would ask Elliott to step outside of the line. And there would be questions and concerns and meddling in.

Elliott hates meddlers. A lot of 'beezily buzzles,' as little Lori might say.

Perhaps Elliott should try the fish? With some salty cut fries?

His little girls (and the wee one in time) would not ever behave like bad Margaret. If Elliott were to ever bring them out? But no, he would be much too nervous to expose them to the light. There are too many possibilities of things going wrong. The world is a dangerous place full of meddlesome people and pointy sharp things. The girls (and the wee one) are happy below with Elliott to protect and Elliott to provide and Elliot to...

He's breathing again in that way that he does, with the itching getting virulent and Margaret's stares and should he have them leave off the onions? The girls might not welcome them. Not that they'd complain about whatever Elliott brought home. That lesson had been instilled ages ago.

Now it is Margaret's turn. Listen to the way the mother speaks to her, cooing and cajoling as if Margaret were in charge.

Elliott breathes in that way that he does, and Margaret is screaming now. "Sorry, sorry," the dim-mommy says. "She's had a long day."

If Margaret were Elliott's, she'd have an even longer night.

The itching and the breathing and the bobbing of heads and Margaret's screaming and the smiling clerk with his black cap and the 'stop it, precious' and choices and signs and the stainless steel slab and the dolls and the children back at home, his children back home, Elliot's children waiting back home. (*He mustn't he mustn't he*) Elliot loves them, cares for them, needs them, wants them, from the moment that each of them came to his door, once bright-shiny-faces and the wee one now, too. Perhaps Elliott will get them all shakes. A 'nilla like Margaret is screaming about. Shakes and fries and nuggets of chicken, take the treats home to his precious ones there. They will be so grateful.

And Elliott breathes in that way that he does.

Margaret drags her mother away. Margaret, Margaret, Margie, Marge, tasting her name like the food they'll consume.

Elliot breathes in that way that he does. He itches his palm. And then it is time.

"Do you know what you'd like?" comes the query.

No, Elliott wants to respond.

Yes, Elliott wants to respond.

Margaret, Elliott wants to respond. 🎲

G.L. CONNORS

THE WOLF IN ME

This madness.
This wolf that won't let go
won't absolve me or allow me to forgive —
If I could shoot it in the heart, I would.
No. That would be suicide.
It loves me; it does.

Its teeth that shine, its teeth that lick.
A purpling wound, a twilight.
Deep velvet pleasure. And then

the shame. I'm no crazier than our shattered
precious world. Its light that explodes
leaving darkness behind.

40

I tried, you know. Tried turning away from its raw
hot breath. Tried locking the windows.
Folded and creased a hundred origami doves.

For an hour, maybe two, safety visited me.
Hah. Looked in the mirror and there —
my skin peeling away, the wolf crawling out.

KIRK McDAVITT

TASTES

I've never been able to decide on one thing. It doesn't matter if we're talking jobs, food, travel, books, or movies. There has never been one of any style or genre to which I can fully commit. I want it all. Or, at least, I want to know part of it all. I want tastes: the full spectrum.

And when it comes to music—it's the same deal.

My first musical awakening came via cassette when I was thirteen. My family was freshly back in Michigan after three years of Tennessee strangeness that had left me with dangerous reserves of angst (something about being derided by my eighth-grade history teacher for being a "Yankee" that I could never wrap my head around). I was hanging out with Doug, my new best friend. His buddy in Florida had recently sent him a simple black cassette. One side was labeled "Dead Kennedys," and the other side "Agent Orange."

If you've ever said, "What? You've never heard of them?" and then had the pleasure of immediately turning someone on to something you knew would blow their mind, then you can imagine the look in Doug's eye when he placed that tape into the stereo and pressed play.

41

When the sound came out of the speakers my whole body expanded. It was as if I had taken my first deep breath after years of taking only shallow puffs. I'm certain my eyes must have dilated and my pulse surely quickened. An image formed in my mind of a basement or a garage or a concrete cube tucked far beneath the surface of conscious thought. Shadowy figures manipulated instruments I vaguely understood, in ways I couldn't comprehend.

A year before this turning point I had a brush with a similar sentiment when my copy of Motley Crue's *Shout at the Devil* arrived from my family's cassette club. In that case, however, my fascination had more to do with the imagery on the cover of the leather-clad rockers all dolled up, shouting at the devil and helter skeltering. But when I listened to it the music was too produced, the distortion too thin, and the shtick too cartoonish, even for my twelve-year-old mind.

No no no. This was something different. This was something that came from dark places. The lo-fi cassette with its hiss and warble only added to the magic. For the first time I understood that low quality could mean better output. I understood that people made music with absolutely no intention of reaching a wide audience. It even seemed to me that they were actually saying, "Don't listen to this!" And by drinking it in I was defying their wishes and also giving them exactly what they wanted.

It was a heady mixture for me to handle. I didn't know people were allowed to sing like that. Initially I couldn't fully figure out if they were serious or not. But it didn't matter. I felt sweaty and swoony and like, "Oh my god, why am I only discovering this now? What else have I been missing?"

For the first time in my life I was hearing music that I wanted to play at maximum volume. I wanted my parents to hear it and tell me to turn it down (they were actually pretty cool about it), I wanted the neighbors to hear it and bitch about the racket (that may have happened).

I wanted to know every word. I learned every word. I realized I could harmonize with Jello Biafra and Mike Palm because I had learned how to sing from the gut.

The music fueled our reckless skateboarding ambitions and armed us against the witless normals, and it was liberating to such a degree that all music since has essentially fallen under its umbrella. That cassette is the original compass point.

Occasionally, I get out in public and play records. And when I do, I'm all over the place from folk to rock to jazz to noise to railroad sounds to the odd sonata and always something a little funky and often some of the boom boom boom. If people get to dancing, and I feel they've arrived at that total surrender moment, there's a record I'm always slowly reaching for called *Murder was the Bass*. It's big room techno at its finest and guaranteed to get people moving and provide for that hands in the air moment.

But personally, in private, when I'm weary of sifting through the endless digital catalogue of all music ever created, when I must take a break from expanding my horizons or filling in knowledge gaps, when there is only one longing left to be obliged, I reach for *Give Me Convenience or Give Me Death* and *Living in Darkness*, and all tastes are satisfied. 🏵

JEANNE WILKINSON

A Tale of Two Concerts

An adapted excerpt from the as-yet-unpublished memoir:
1969: My Year with a San Francisco Drug Dealer

When we finally arrive at Altamont, we're not even close. We walk and walk past hundreds, thousands of cars until we get to the great grassy knoll with the stage at the bottom, far away from us.

So many people. Too many. I don't think I would have been a happy camper at Woodstock, that giant refugee camp sporting a fabulous sound system along with endless mud and mess and trash and people, people, people. But unlike a real refugee settlement, Woodstock closed after a long muddy weekend because everyone had somewhere else to go. So for those few precious days, it was a *miracle of peace and love* that all those people so close together for so long in such conditions never let things descend into mayhem and murder! Wow!

But wasn't the peace in large part due to the planning, the infrastructure — sketchy but there (and totally non-existent here at Altamont) — of doctors and volunteers who helped people through bad trips, birthings, bugs? And the Hog Farm-er's free food tent?

And wasn't the peace due to the far-fucking-out, never-before-never-again music, mesmerizing Siren songs sent out into the sodden green-going-brown world: Richie Havens calling out for "A Little Help From My Friends"; Arlo Guthrie's "Amazing Grace"; Joan Baez lifting her voice to "Oh, Happy Day"; Canned Heat's "Let's Work Together"? And Jimi Hendrix ending it on a mud-covered Monday morning with the "Star Spangled Banner" of Star-Spangled-fucking-Banners? Music as an ecstatic inflammation of the soul, hot pulses burning tiger bright into each mud-spattered, starry-eyed head? A clarion call to ancient sleeping deities: oh, come out and play, ye gods of the rain and the clotted sky and goddesses of the meadow and the slippery earth, come and charge the air with your electric presence for a precious moment, this moment, so we can remember and reshape and rejoin and live in the everlasting hum of now and forever, each of us our own axis mundi joining heaven and earth with an undulating spine and a dance of oscillating joy?

Sisters and brothers, let us now join hands and change the world.

Okay, okay, so maybe Woodstock was a miracle of sorts, and had I been there, I may have stepped over some internal barbed-wire fence, let go of my need for individuality, for privacy, for all those precious Americanisms that keep us just free enough to choose which ruthless corporate interest we wish to be manipulated by, and I'd have become one with the slippery mass of blissed-out, music-drenched souls, letting the wet clinging mud and the guitars and drums and voices mold me into one of the People of the Clay, the People of the Song, the People of the Vast Churning Meadow of Mud.

But here at Altamont, even out in the hinterlands, perched high up on the lip of the bowl, we know we're not in Oz anymore. Or Woodstock. No rainbow, no rain, dry as an old bone and the vibe seems dry, too, taut and torn, ragged, off-key. The big, cranky sound system goes dead for long stretches, severing the umbilical cord of music that sustains us. And instead of Wavy Gravy keeping the peace with "*please* don't do *this*, *please* do *that* instead," we have security courtesy of the Hell's Angels, paid with $500 worth of beer.

Crosby, Stills, Nash and Young come on but seem tense, off their game. After they warble their last note, we're in for a long, nerve-wracking wait.

Bring on the Dead!

We don't know that the Grateful Dead have decided not to come out and play. We wait-wait-wait-wait-wait-wait, the crowd-buzz sounding more and more like cicadas gone mad, a guitar string about to snap, tension rising with the full moon that sneaks up behind the hillside like a grinning devil's head. The super-stoned-out crowd is flirting with hysteria when lights blaze on the stage far, far away and a little silken figure, black on one side and red on the other, begins to prance around to the tune of "Jumpin' Jack Flash."

His Satanic Majesty has commenced leaping and twitching, flapping like fire in the midst of the demon-choir of

Angels that surrounds him, and the crowd stops holding its collective breath. Ahhh. Mick will take care of every-thing. The Stones are tough dudes. They are magic men. But during the third song, the music grinds to a halt. Mick's manic gyrating call to *name the evil one!* stops dead, his silken wings go limp, and he's on the microphone sounding nervous. Sounding whiny. Sounding like he's not tough *or* magical, calling on his brothers and sisters to *cool out over there, all right?*

"Sympathy for the Devil" may have been satire, but when the Devil hears you singing an ode to him, maybe he doesn't need to be invited twice. Maybe he thinks it's "satyrical"—ha!

The Stones begin again, making it to song seven, "Under My Thumb," before Mick has to call for a doctor, an ambulance. Miraculously, panic does not ensue. The music goes on. The music prevails, but the grand finale, "Street Fighting Man," falls pretty falsely on our freaked-out ears. While rumors of violence and mayhem ripple through the night, we walk away under a full fat moon in Scorpio that floods the land with cold dead light, all of us save four: one killed by an Angel, three others in accidents.

Altamont is labeled the anti-Woodstock, the bad, sad end of the waning Summer of Love, the last crashing stop of the '60's peace and love train. But maybe it's not about peace and love at all. Maybe it's about music. About music's power to create realities, to connect us to what's out there, and what's *in here*. For better or worse.

Woodstock was a clarion call of one sort, and Altamont another entirely. ◈

SALLY LIPTON DERRINGER

WHATEVER GETS YOU THROUGH THE NIGHT

What words do you need when you're trying
not to drop the house on your back, your shoulders
bruised, a hard rain falling? Neil Young was on
the stereo when you swapped your innocence
for the winding road, something starting, the
damage done. And later, down by the river,
your future rose and fell with the rhythm of Dr.
King's speech on the tape deck, a double fantasy
of black and tan, a love supreme.
Everyone smiled as Debussy played and you promised
a thing called love, the wild air pleading for
your attention, his arm holding you in place.
You can't handle therapy: the sound of your own
voice blabbing its pathetic story. What lyrics now?
Certainly not your son's CD of tender love songs,
his earnest voice something that shouldn't
be betrayed. Should you put on some Miles
Davis, a little Bonnie Raitt to accompany your blue
mood, so you can wallow in the feeling of being pinned
down to this bed you've made, the absence
of where you were going?

48

This poem was composed using the following song titles:

Whatever Gets You Through the Night — John Lennon
A Hard Rain's A-Gonna Fall — Bob Dylan
The Long and Winding Road — the Beatles
Gonna Be Startin' Somethin' — the Jackson 5
The Needle and the Damage Done — Neil Young
Down by the River — Neil Young
Double Fantasy — John Lennon/Yoko Ono
Black and Tan Fantasy — Duke Ellington
A Love Supreme — John Coltrane
Thing Called Love — Bonnie Raitt
Blue Moods — Miles Davis

SALLY LIPTON DERRINGER

49

CEZANNE ALEXANDER

Advent Calendar

December 1, 2017

I am alone this December, cloistered in a stranger's
Airbnb apartment to finish my memoir. A package arrives
addressed to me, wrapped in worn brown paper, post-
marked Nov 28, 1978. The return address is the first I ever
learned. The handwriting is my mother's—eerie, as she
died four years ago this month. I place it on my borrowed
desk and as I watch, the package unwraps itself. A farrago
of parts and pieces fall out; they untangle and assemble.
The jumble arranges into a model of my childhood home.
Numbers appear on doors, furniture, secret hiding places.
It is an Advent Calendar. It completes itself in a crackle
of red and white sparks.

   I peer through a tiny window into a miniature replica of
my bedroom. The number One is my old dresser. I focus
on it and POOF! A ribboned box appears, here, in this
apartment. Inside is a snow globe. It is full of my tears.
I shake it. My naïve, youthful aspirations glitter and swirl
around changing images of things won and things lost.

Musepaper Story Prize, Volume 1, 2019
'Advent Calendar' © 2017 Cezanne Alexander

December 2nd

Today I tilt and turn my home looking for number Two.
I find it on the backside of my parent's bathroom door.
Blink and another box materializes. Wound inside is my
mother's bathrobe sash: tattered and makeup-stained.
I knot it around my waist. Honeysuckle. Liverwurst, Bach,
Sunday school; a perfectionist, worn out.

December 3rd

An illuminated Three, gilded vermilion, glows in the living
room bookshelf. Before I reach, I wonder which book it
will be: The first to make me cry? The one I read again and
again? Hemingway? Steinbeck? Shakespeare? A wicked
little smile and one eyebrow up — the one worth the
most on eBay? With a foul sulfur belch the illuminated
Three disappears.

December 4th

No Four. Did I break the spell? I move my hands over my
home. I sense warm, cold, very cold, warmer. The sensation
leads me to the front porch. Hot! Hot! Something shiny
caught between the boards. I nudge and cajole it to the
edge. My father's lucky Indian Head coin. I'm the one
who lost it, but accused my best friend of stealing it. My
brother said that's why she moved away.

December 5th

Dark, lumpy, and a bit moldy. Number Five is on the kitchen counter. Fruitcake. Penance? I chew and swallow, a hint of bourbon.

December 6th

Six is Dad's workbench. With a static sputter, his old AM radio plays carols: little drummer boys wait for Santa's reindeer.

December 7th

Sevens are everywhere. I try a two-handed swirl. Holiday lotto tickets flutter onto this desk. I can hear Grandma saying, "Gambling's the devil's work." I scratch, but do not win.

December 8th

Eight is Mom's KitchenAid. I wish for... a battered 3×5 card.

> *Joe Froggers*
> *Mix butter, sugar, molasses, and dark rum.*
> *Add ginger, cloves, nutmeg, allspice...*

A timer rings in the apartment. I smell spices. I open the oven—inside, a dozen ginger men.

December 9th–12th

This morning's weather is frightful. I'm delighted to find

my childhood home all decorated. White lights, scissored snowflakes, a tree with silver and red balls, handmade ornaments, and tiny birds. For the next four days, while the winter storm rages, I tap a decoration and my rented halls are decked. I save the tree for last. I wish for someone to share it with.

December 13th

The old rotary phone in our hallway rings. Now it's here, on the desk. So awkward, I slip my finger into the holes and dial our old number, long disconnected. My brother answers! We haven't spoken in years. We talk for hours but make no promises.

December 14th

I work all day on my memoir, skipping breakfast and lunch. The light fades and I'm starving. The fridge won't open. I eye the Calendar. Yes, #14 is our old fridge, the mustard-colored wheezer we scrimped for two years to replace. The apartment's refrigerator sputters. A picked-over spiral ham sits alone, half-covered in foil. I fork off a gelatinous slice and return to writing.

December 15th

Fifteen is my bedroom. A tiny box appears. Tucked in black starry velvet is a waning crescent. I recall sleepless nights: stories finished undercover, Grandpa in a rented hospital bed, a teenage slumber party, my deflowering, and journaling—always journaling.

December 16th

The coatrack. I open the box. My father's scarf, a dark tartan. It still smells of pipe tobacco, Old Spice, and snooker.

December 17th

My closet. The apartment lights dim, all my devices synchro-play Handel's Messiah. The stolen burgundy choir robe — hidden all these years — drops in a heavy pile at my feet, followed by a well-worn hymnal. God and sinners reconciled.

December 18th

Number 18 the loveseat. A caress. A sprig of mistletoe — crushed. Under it is a folded, crumpled note. I look at my left hand, at my never ringed-finger. What if? The tears fall.

December 19th

I consider smashing the Calendar. I don't look for #19.

December 20th

Two Xs notch my secret hiding place under the stairs. I trace the Xs, a box appears. Inside is a pellucid beryl palantír — a seeing stone. I gaze into it and recognize scenes from my past: old playmates and teachers, aunts and uncles, grandparents, Mother waving, Dad a step behind. All dead. It connects me to we.

Winter Solstice

My mother's favorite day, the year's longest night. Outside, thorny twigs scrape the porch. The apartment's desk is covered in Peace Rose petals.

December 22nd

Our hall closet. Wrapping paper, curling ribbon, presents given and received. I drop $20 into the bell ringer's red bucket at the grocery store.

December 23rd

The mantelpiece. A row of candles. Now they light this desk. I work late, until they gutter.

Christmas Eve

Our stairwell. A family photo dated December, 1978. My memoir is finished: "To my mother and father."

Christmas Day

The Calendar is gone. 🎲

CONSTANCE CAMPANA

LITTLE HOUSE

I haven't had a home since I was 25. Not really. That's
when my mother died. She had cancer, and one day, more
than a year before her death, I stood at mid-day looking
out the front window of the house my husband and I were
renting and imagined her dead. I panicked and called
my older brother, as I sometimes did when I was afraid,
always forgetting that his talent was objectivity—and
forgetting, mostly, that his response would not help, and
at first it didn't. He said, "This is what happens. We knew
this. We knew she wouldn't have that long." I remember
saying, "Uh huh," as though I knew it, too. Then I remembered why I had called and added, "Yeah, but I really
imagined it. Like, all the way." My brother said, "Well,"
and then softly, "I know." And then I was grateful for the
sound of his voice, and that he could put aside the facts
he relied on. I had not called my older brother for facts.

The fact—the *real* fact—was my sudden knowledge
that soon, I wouldn't have a Mom. And we were close, my
mother and I. I had one child and another due soon and
I needed my mother. When she went out on errands, she'd
call and ask, "Do you want to come along?" I could talk to

my mother; I *liked* talking to my mother. We didn't always agree—Mom was opinionated—but I didn't mind. I knew that she loved me irrevocably. I think I knew I'd never have *that* again—that whole love that would never turn away. And in that first moment of knowing that my mother would not remain a walking, talking person alive in the world, like the people I saw walking by on our sidewalk, a new feeling fluttered in my stomach and it wasn't good.

People sometimes hinted that I was "sheltered" and I certainly was. But I knew of no other way to be alive. My brothers left home and went to school and began, I guess, *developing*. I got married and figured I'd gone far enough. I was done. My mother stabilized me and made me feel brave. I had no idea I wasn't brave, nor stable. I would find all of this out. I would *develop*, though to me, the word implies something fluid, like a sauce that gradually thickens. And maybe that's what happens to some people. After my mother died, the earth gave way beneath me more than once, and each time I'd think: *how do I do this? How do I go on in life?* I think all of my ideas of home began dying the moment I knew my mother was, which is what makes the memory of one of our last car rides sad—so sad that I'd forgotten it until a few years ago.

One day in August, three months before my mother died, she drove out to some place I'd never been. She parked alongside a huge expanse of green grass, like a small field, and farther back sat a small white house. "That's the house," she said. "That's the one I keep thinking of for you and Mike." It's hard for me to remember she was still selling houses—that she had the specs on that little white house. I rolled down the window and the heat of that August—that thick, humid air—poured in and is forever fused with my view of that house. At first I was confused; I didn't know how things happened. How does one buy a house? How would my mother buy us a house? Because that's what she was saying: *That little house is the house I want to buy for you and Mike.* She didn't say those words, but I knew what she meant.

But this is what I mean: Even though nothing new had happened—the cancer that would reappear hadn't shown up yet—I felt the house to be a wish my mother was showing me. As though really she was saying: *This is the house I would have bought for you and Mike, if I hadn't gotten sick.* Or: *This is the house I would buy for you if I wasn't going to die.* So I couldn't take it in, except in my heart. And the house has stayed, locked there, because I could hear in her voice that this was what she wanted, not what she could do. There is nothing sadder than listening to the threads of what is left of someone's life, like unrequited love, still alive, still leaning toward what can never be. *I want you to have something,* she was saying.

I have thought about that house lately—distant and white and heavy with heat—and I make myself walk inside of it. It is empty, of course, and for some reason

I am wearing my mother's blue bathrobe—the one she wore constantly the last month of her life. The floors are wood, and an arched molding separates the living room and the dining room. I know if I go further, I'll see the kitchen, but I can't make myself move. I can't go up the staircase to the bedrooms, either. Mike is dead and we've been divorced for years; my children are grown and living in different states. But the feeling of us as a family in this house is so strong that it overwhelms me. I see the basket of toys, the rugs, the sofa, the dining room table, which is set for dinner. I hear myself in the kitchen, cooking, talking on the phone. I know what she wanted to give me and why: a piece of life with a bottom that wouldn't fall out. A place on this earth to contain me, when she no longer could.

CONSTANCE CAMPANA

SUSAN MAEDER

SALT: A HOMECOMING

It was Penelope's job to wait. And weave. Or so we think.
Who writes of Penelope, her many-syllabled reality?
Who wants to know what she had for breakfast the morning
that One-Eyed Clod was trying to finish her husband off?

Soft bread? No. Grain's scarce and the land is full of discord.
The servants aren't even up yet, and the suitors
are still snoring, sorting out odds in their dreams, casting lots:

> *two black: the ship's gone down, she'll have me;*
> *one black, one white: he's on his way, hold off;*
> *two white: get out before sunrise and the trumpeting starts.*

She settles for something with salt:
Plank of cod, smoked whole, still gilled and silvery,
is placed before her.

60

The sea's outside the door, chuffing gently at the shore.
Her heart-shaped companion, the harp, lists against the cold rock wall.
The old wise maid's made honey sticks, stiff reeds poked into the
hives to capture some sweetness. She's stuck them like flowers

in a vase on the table, the tips of gritty gold straight up,
like tapers to ignite. She brings a shawl against the cold
and drapes her mistress. She mentions the gods and withdraws.

Penelope alone in the pre-dawn.
Tangled hair. A bit rank from lack of hygiene.
Finger tips calloused from working the loom and the harp.

She's growing hunched from clutching her shawl
against the perpetual damp.
She's no Greta Garbo.

Her legend beauty is Power, you see,
not the curds-and-peach glow of the starlet.
She's coarse, mottled, her knuckles are starting to bulge.

But she's practiced in Magic,
If there's a crystal sphere anywhere near,
you can bet she's looked into it:

Ship, ship, lulling on the flat sea.

One time, something hard to decipher having to do with pigs...

...a feast with roasts and figs (a momentary salivating response.)

A murder of crows. She sees them as a mutinous crew,
descending, shredding the sails in their fury,

One whole summer of hot wind, endless grappling with riggings,
eternal sun filling the sky.

Salt.

She sees it all then turns away from the crystal ball
and there is no spouse. No ship. No harrowing waves
or narrow channels.

Another flake of smoky fish.
The honey insults her ruined tooth.
She refuses to wince, she's grown that tough.

She tosses a tidbit to the mewling cat and fingers her chin
which may or may not be sprouting a hair.

She doesn't care. The sun's coming up.
Something is going to happen today.

He's coming home, of course. We've read it a thousand times,
and each time the heart jumps, doesn't it?

Imagine the trumpets sounding as the ships touch land,
all the townsfolk shuffling down to the shore, ripe for stories
of glory and gore, hungry for booty.

When Odysseus slumps off the ship he's grizzled
and grim as a beggar. Twenty odd years
have passed and soon he'll be face to face with his beloved.

She's wizened and lacking a primary tooth or two.
Nothing to hide the wrinkles,
no lotions or potions, no scented oils.

To hell with it, she'd told herself when the last suitor
compared her to some plump fruit. She'd caught her face
in a silver urn and set her course.
Salt, she said.

But here they are now, circling each other.
Sun-shrunk and brown as a leather strap—
he's smaller than she! The toll the sea took
is the shortened bones and the lack of bravura.

He's thinking "husk" as he appraises her.
His lovely Penelope. She of the shimmering hair and the turn
of hip that could sting him with desire. The fleshy lips.
The pointed chin. The pearly...

She wants to burst into flames
to show him what she's become: this force!
This fire will undo you!
Your wounds are nothing!
Your real travail is just begun!

He wants to lie down. He broke his collarbone
holding the ship's course through the rocks.
He's bruised and battle-scarred.

Didn't there used to be wine?
Is their home really this small?
Where's the dog?
Who is this woman, staring him down?

And then it begins: *Drum... Drum drum...*

Oh no, she thinks, no!
Lust is as dead as the old goat that tripped on a knuckle of rock
then tumbled, slid, and landed with a thud on the shore...

...Isn't it?

But here we still are. And the stars are coming out.
Look, my love, the Scorpion, see? The Centaur. And there's the goat,
replaced on the rock, so noble, tenacious and dear.
And there! — the huge star that saw you home.

He unwraps her.

She hasn't lost her sense of touch, our Penelope.
Her bent fingers' callused tips are alive with the radar of lust.

This chest with its ragged scar where the Cyclops ripped at him.
Brown buds of pointless nipples —
(her own have begun to clear their throats and sing.)

The — oh — still tender hollow
where the throat keeps the voice hidden inside.
Her tongue wants to rest there, exchanging salts.

Her head is full of firecrackers, but her heart...
her heart is a fig held over the flame until it puffs and swells
and threatens to burst.

What a pittance of mercy the gods dole out, but
the old rugged pumps and valves deliver one more time.

Drum drum...

O Odysseus sublime luck brought you here.
Look in her eyes — quick —
and see your own staring back. Now say yes. Yes.
Say yes.

Now the part where the moon slides out,
the stars do a few pliés and patter off stage left.
The lizards scuttle for shelter.

Not that it's easy,
the giving up and over after all these years.
Don't forget the crystal sphere and what she saw there.
Or the nectar he's grown accustomed to.

But let's hope they defy the odds,
and that the moon will hold its place in the sky long enough
to show them where they finally might arrive: home.

NATALIE MUCKER

ENSŌ

At the beginning of Luke Ossani's yoga class, I am not entirely myself. I've somehow lost touch with half of me, the peaceful half, the part that keeps me from quitting adulthood, buying a one-way ticket to Morocco, or drinking one to five glasses of wine per night. He teaches at my small-town studio once a week: Saturday 8:00 a.m. For this I am grateful. I practice with the other instructors, but it is Luke's class that I need on Saturday mornings, to haul off the week's worth of tension that my peaceful self has left the rest of me to carry, alone.

Luke is six-foot-something, moderately inked, with a wispy brown beard that sways near his sternum.

"Good morning, Natalie," he says in his pleasant deep voice. I huff into the lobby and mumble my hello. It's cold—stupid cold—and I am stupid grumpy.

I remove my boots and am annoyed at the snow dripping off them. I'm annoyed at my parka's testy zipper, the way I know my hair looks under my hat. I'm annoyed at the injustices of the world, the results of last year's election, the boy who broke my heart when I was eleven.

I find an antisocial corner to claim and unroll my mat. The yogis brave enough to speak to me receive my grumpy greetings in return. I lie down with my arms over my eyes and try to wiggle warmth into my numb toes. A melody that my peaceful self would enjoy makes its way from the speakers, offering a sip of tranquility—which I refuse. My week was too stressful; I have too much to do today. I can't be appeased by some song.

Luke joins us from the lobby, taking his place in the front of the room. He lowers himself to the floor and faces us, a gentle smile beneath kind brown eyes.

"Good morning, everyone, and welcome. How's everybody doing today?" Pamela replies amidst nods and murmurs. "We're good, Luke. How are you?" "I'm great, Pam. Thank you for asking."

I like Pamela. She's over twice my age and exudes a confidence that I respect and admire, but how dare she speak for me? I'm not "good." No one is safe from the wrath of my mood. Luke turns his twinkling eyes on me, like he suspects as much, and smiles.

"Let's get started, shall we? Everyone take a comfortable seat, cross-legged, on your knees, whatever feels right for you this morning."

We shift and shuffle. I sit one way, then another, unable to find comfort.

"Let's all take a moment to get in touch with our breath. I would invite you to close your eyes."

Gladly, I think, shutting them on the world.

"Deep breath in."

I hear the room's collective inhale. I feel like I'm wearing an invisible corset, laced up by my ego and yanked tight by my neuroses.

"Full breath out." I do my best.

We start slow, rolling the shoulders, the neck, arms reaching high, gentle twists of the spine. My peaceful self sends up a smoke signal, but I'm still mad at her for abandoning me. "Across the Universe" by Fiona Apple comes on, and I can't help but silently mouth the words in my downward dog.

With his feel-good playlist and soothing sentiments, Luke lures me out of the darkness, as he does many Saturdays. How does he do it? More importantly, how do I wind up in this mood so often? It's like I peer into an ominous doorway on Monday, wander into the dungeon on Tuesday, trip and fall and lie paralyzed in self-pity on Wednesday, try to rally on Thursday, only to find on Friday that I'm too late—the door's been locked.

Yoga reminds me of what's beyond the dungeon, of all that isn't grumpy and cold. Each flow we take knocks the rust loose from my bones. Each stretch lengthens my wadded-up muscles. My blood warms in the stillness of each pose. I inhale the good life and exhale the stress. My peaceful self cheers me on, and I hold out my hand to her.

Luke cracks a joke and I laugh alongside my friends. I sway to the music, feeling balanced and free. I can move however I want and never fall. If I do, who cares. It's magic, this class. There's sweat on my forehead, so I know I did some of the work. My teacher lit the path of escape for me, but it turns out I held the key to the dungeon door.

By the time we reach savasana, our final resting pose, I'm practically comatose with giddiness. To-do lists don't matter; words are just mushy goodness, like cookies taken from the oven before they're fully baked. Warm and sweet and gooey. My body melts into the Earth. My mind is relieved of tension. *Hey, girl,* I whisper—my peaceful self returned. I am whole again.

We roll up our mats in the serene atmosphere of our making. Luke speaks with a new student about her experience.

"No, you won't find a lot of cardio in my class," he agrees. "It's a different kind of workout, more of the mind—" he pauses, and I glance up from my corner, curious. His eyes alight when he finds what he was searching for in his head.

"When I do yoga, I feel that it's easier to be a good person, a good father, husband, teacher—" The girl smiles, unconvinced. I feel a twinge of annoyance, but he shrugs good-naturedly, "—at least for the next twelve hours or so." His goofy laugh fills the room, obliterating any trace of my bad mood.

And that's how I end sixty minutes with Luke Ossani: like myself again, my better self…at least for the next twelve hours or so. 🝊

This is the author's first literary award and her first work to appear in a print publication.

HANA ROWAN-SEDDON

EXPAT

This time you've been moved to another continent as well as country, and the change in climate is making your skin reptilian. You've been showering with your head down lately, watching your feet slowly change from golden to sheep's-brain pink, and helplessness slips down the drain with the water, yeah, you watch it go down.

Your new friend has her warm palm flat on the small of your back and propels you forward into dark and noise. It's a depressing country, immutable grey chill to it, but the kids here keep it at bay as best they can. Another one of your new friends is upstairs, banging and kicking at her own unyielding bedroom door, a bra strap hanging loosely by her elbow, her mouth open and full of howls of fury you can't hear.

It's like she's yelling at herself on the other side of the door and it's off-putting, makes you feel a bit sick as you're guided deeper into the house.

You and your new friends wear the same kinds of dresses and drink the same kind of alcohol—you've taken pains to ensure you slot right in. There are less people making

69

out at this party than there used to be in the hot fever kick of your old country, there are fewer dark corners to retreat into. It's like Big Brother here in your new friends' house, square-bright phone torches flashing all over the place—no one can do anything without being filmed. It's a better surveillance system than the FBI, honest to god. Tomorrow you will watch the you of tonight about twenty separate but identical times, you'll watch yourself like TV, like someone anonymous wrote your script for you, penned Authentic Teen Dialogue. Yeah, tomorrow you won't remember doing anything that your phone screen plays back.

This morning it was your third day at your new job. They gave you a fleece as well as a jumper because the establishment was cavernous with big glass doors opening and closing constantly. Outside the doors was an inflatable snowman that was wired to shiver uncontrollably. It always seemed to be juddering in your periphery, seeming to you that it was having some sort of medical catastrophe, a death rattle. You sat at the tills all day on a chair that didn't roll as much as wobble, and was covered in a scratchy, conductive kind of fabric, kind of like the jumper they gave you. An eerie, meandering version of "Greensleeves" played through the overhead speakers all day and it was so deliciously depressing you even managed to enjoy it for the first hour.

A Christmas tree in a cardboard box lay on a trolley in front of your till, waiting to be collected. You kicked your heel against the chair until it ached, sat on your hands until the chair was imprinted in them, took a bath in the overhead strip lights; they washed over you thorough as anything. They were floodlights, they were too bright to even be a color you could discern. In the distance, at the back of the shop, it was dark, and in the middle distance, there was the shop's own gigantic Christmas tree—a sentinel, decorated only with lights that hadn't been switched on. It watched you, darkly, and you watched it back darker, "Greensleeves" stuttering and repeating itself, white shirt collar turning your neck pink and red.

Tonight you're sitting outside at the party with just a dress on, but you've had enough to drink that you're disconnected from the cold now so it's fine, you can leave your jacket buried underneath all the others on that kitchen chair.

One of your new friends careens past you and lands on all fours in the grass, starts to vomit. You get up out of your seat. The party's been going on long enough that the grass is frost-encrusted, thousands of little sparks of cold, and they twinkle like fairy lights as you lurch towards the new friend. She holds a hand up to ward you off, long strand of whatever came up swaying from her mouth—the tendril hangs with a glint on it as it reflects the phone-torch light of someone taking a photo of her. You sit back down again, so implausibly heavy and leaden that you're not sure how the chair holds you. Another new friend collapses onto your lap, hand around your neck, cheek against your forehead. This new friend of yours is a prophet. She always knows what's going to happen before it does. Her finger is a pretty shade of lilac from the cold and points without accuracy but with melodrama, points through the window into the house where the couple she knew would get together are getting together. At least four different phones are filming them but they're aware of that, yeah, they know.

This one song comes on for the third time that night and there's a collective yell. You try to glean as much catharsis as you can from the moment but you're bone-dry, you're all out of stock. New friend is still on your lap and you feel really quite untethered so you just watch her black-ringed eyes, watch the shapes her face makes as she talks to you.

You're rid of the mosquitoes and the rolling, itching sweat now, at least—you should think about that, that's something you should try to focus on.

Damp wooden chairs and your new friends, three different layers of chatter that over-arch and undercut each other like a tangle of motorways. Your breath clouds and you forget it's the cold—in the moment you justify it as ashes and embers in your stomach being turned over, giving off one last flush of warmth. 🎲

This is the author's first literary award and her first work to appear in a print publication.

KEITH MARK GABOURY

BEGINNINGS

Can I travel back to the womb,
back to the female zygote
of my conception
when my penis popped out
like a hibiscus through hungry soil.
Yes the cellular shells of you, me,
Mary the turtle hoarder
all multiplied into four-limbed spawn.
How blessed to swim
in a sea of amniotic fluid
without a neurological bother
over raising
a resilient dalmatian
before graduating
to a family of four.
I return home
to Sam barking in the mud room
as your body builds a femur.
Through the kitchen window,
a honeysuckle sapling
vaults towards our common sky.

74

TERRI TRESPICIO

THE CRIPPLE MAKES A WISH

It didn't happen in the way that other
folks will have you think: a flash of light,
a giant earthquake rumbling through your bones.

I simply did what I was told and rose
like leavened bread out of the useless husk.
The healer's face, lit from within, had smiled.

"Take heart, my son," he told me. "Your sins
are washed away; pick up your bed and walk."
And there I stood, on two strong legs, with arms

that until then, I'd lived my life without.
A woman fainted. I began to sway
when both my brothers caught me by my shoulders,

the two of them like planted wooden stakes
that train new stems upward. I turned and left
amidst the naked stares that startled me,

pious praise, tinged with a shade of fear.
And things were never quite the same again.
Before the Nazarene had come to town,

Musepaper Poem Prize, Volume 1, 2019
"The Cripple Makes a Wish" © 2017 Terri Trespicio

people used to ask me if I wished
that I had fingers, if I ever dreamed
of running. "Does a lizard wish to fly,"

I said, "Do tadpoles dream of feathered wings?"
And like a wingless, earth-bound beast,
I'm ill-prepared for this strange flight—

would gladly trade these heavy limbs
to be carried to the river when the white
hot peak of day has passed, and left,

to drift up off my cot; lifted by the gentle
current like a single gilded leaf,
cradled in its mighty, rippled palm. 🔯

Jesus heals the cripple, Matthew 9:1-3

NINA GABY

The Sum of

its Parts

The setting: A Men's Co-Occurring Therapy Group takes
place in an 80+ bed, rural addiction facility, in a small,
snow-covered state, in the freshly painted almost-purple,
"Wild Wisteria" office of the psychiatric nurse practitioner,
who at the moment is screaming silently in her head. Her
brains are still bouncing from an hour-long commute
while listening to NPR. Having the radio on the whole
time was probably a mistake. She is feeling most things
are a mistake, currently jealous of the Facebook posts she
read this morning over coffee from soon to be ex-pats
getting out of harm's way, or friends with various inher-
itances, retirements, better luck. But there's no time for
that. She has more pressing issues: a full folder of psych
referrals and right now a roomful of addicts she is paid
reasonably well to deal with.

  The purple office sits smack in the intersection of two
men's units. A banner hangs on one wall: *"Be the change*

Musepaper Essay Prize, Volume 1, 2019
"The Sum of Its Parts" © 2017 Nina Gaby

you want to see in the world." She looks at it so much that she barely sees it anymore. Sometimes she is so preoccupied she doesn't realize her dress is inside out until lunchtime.

The stats, 1: At least 80% of the men who meet criteria for addiction here are from the criminal justice system. Ninety-nine percent are white, the sons of loggers, of farmers, of drunks, of teachers. No one really has time to follow the numbers or interpret the data. That they are mostly white could be significant although she wishes it didn't matter. Sometimes the sheriff comes to shackle someone and take him away. There's a tendency to make metaphors here and the psychiatric nurse practitioner resists the temptation. But today one group member uses the word "comfort" when addressing another who says, and means it, "You're like wrapping me in a blanket." He uses this to describe how it feels to be in treatment in the facility, where shame is neutralized and maybe one can imagine something beyond. She eventually uses the word "metaphor" to describe the process but is unsure if they know what it means.

The atmosphere: The purple office hums with the foot-stomping rhythm of post-acute withdrawal. Of anxiety/fatigue/nausea/delirium. Of sweat. Of neurotransmitters struggling to flow across pathways destroyed by opioids and alcohol and crack and weed. The thrum of trauma. The scent of many men. An absence of despair, at least for today.

This absence speaks to a presence of its own. The walls sigh with relief. She gives the members each a piece of chocolate and asks them to read the messages printed inside the foil wrapper. *Draw yourself a warm bath. Smell the roses. Take the day off! Dance party! Tell someone you love them!* The men get into these lady-like memes, laughingly describe how they would apply them to today, in the treatment facility, four to a room. Not a rose or bathtub in sight. But the chocolate is sweet, and rituals are essential.

A group member says he's never fit in, why would these guys like him after all he's done. He says maybe he should try an antidepressant. He asks for help. His face is open and upturned, a small ray of sun seems to land on him for a moment. The psychiatric nurse practitioner comments on this.

The process: These guys are alive even as their livers turn to mush, veins harden into old garden hoses. Brain arboretum snipped and snapped.

Lines have been crossed or they wouldn't be here. Even so, they are gentle with each other. She bounces back and forth between these worlds.

The stats, 2: In their small state, 2015 claimed 75 dead from opioid overdose. The nurse practitioner had known one of the victims since they were a child. Another was a young woman who had been in and out of treatment since pubescence. Another a sweet, sweet man from her first group years ago. She had a photo he sent from a hike he took with some of the other men, before he died. He was terrified of heights. They hoisted him up at the end and gathered round for the selfie. Familiarity gives these numbers a taste, a smell. Texture. In 2016 the number jumped to 105. And these numbers don't even account for the DUI deaths or the Emergency Room visits or the Department for Children and Families files or the Probation and Parole numbers.

2015: 33,091 dead nationwide from opioids alone.[1] 52,404 all told.[2] And did she just hear, again with the local radio on, that 2016 data jumped 38%?[3]

The prognosis for 2017 is worse.

The metaphor: She is tempted on a bad day to call this spitting in the wind. On a day like today, she comforts herself with platitudes. *Recovery is a journey, not a destination. Keep it simple. One day at a time.*

She thinks she should contact the company that makes the chocolates and give them a whole bunch of ideas for their wrappers. She'd do it for free.

Her role today is as much ambassador as border guard. There was a time long before this when she never would have imagined it.

A large man, nodding precariously from his morning maintenance dose, is propped back up in his seat by his neighbor. He usually doesn't talk much and fights the recommendation that his meds be reduced. He opens his eyes to the blanket metaphor. He adds his own.

He tells us, "This here, this is a safe neighborhood. I can walk the streets at night." He smiles around the purple room, bright and alert before he tips forward again. Murmurings abound. Many neighborhoods are populated by inhospitable guests. The psychiatric nurse practitioner is no stranger to this.

As immigrants, all of us, maybe a sweet minute or two of humanity. She stays put, having shaken off the regret for now. They all have. 🏵

[1] https://www.cdc.gov/drugoverdose/data/statedeaths.html
[2] http://www.asam.org/docs/default-source/advocacy/opioid-addiction-disease-facts-figures.pdf
[3] Vermont Public Radio, 2-16-17

KATHRYN GAHL

40

The day after I visit my daughter in prison
I think of how she is not allowed to handle money
not even go near the vending machines
in the visiting room so it is up to me to scan
the glass boxes, memorize, and
walk back to her to
ask what she wants—pizza or fries—for
there is no fruit amidst Cheetos and Skittles

and I think of fruit, of watching her Papa
put a banana peel in the silverware drawer
when I went to be with him in his last days

at which time he tucked in the banana
with such finesse
before taking off all his clothes
and attempting to button an invisible shirt
around his swollen cancerous belly

It was then he turned to me
lips in a full smile, saying
  I'd like to do it again
  only next time
  I'd like to do it better.

82

Musepaper Poem Prize, Volume 1, 2019
'Forty' © 2017 Kathryn Gahl

In the decade since he died, I think about It
an elusive pronoun that can function by itself or
partake in discourse: was his It my It? Does it matter as
        the past becomes the present
        and tomorrow twists memories
        of windsong and longing

        of the whisper paint made
        when it touched his canvas
        and stayed, of
        Beethoven's Triple Concerto
        washing the walls in a Greenwich Village loft
        where I peeled not pages
in a thesaurus, where I measured not words but flour,
where I fed not my soul but his as I sprinkled
        powdered sugar on homemade crepes suzette

Would I do any of it again?
Only if I were crazy ❧

CONTRIBUTORS

MUSEPAPER 1.0

▲ **Laura Maynard** is a Writer's Craft teacher, living with her husband and son in the beautiful village of Enniskillen, Ontario. She feels lucky to be able to inspire in young people a passion for writing. Laura has published four short stories and is currently working on her first novel.

Jonathan Segol's first writing was as a songwriter in New York and as a journalist for *Street News*. He now teaches writing at Hudson Valley Community College in Troy, NY and has just finished a coming-of-age novel about chop shops, Coney Island, graffiti, and Y2K. ▼

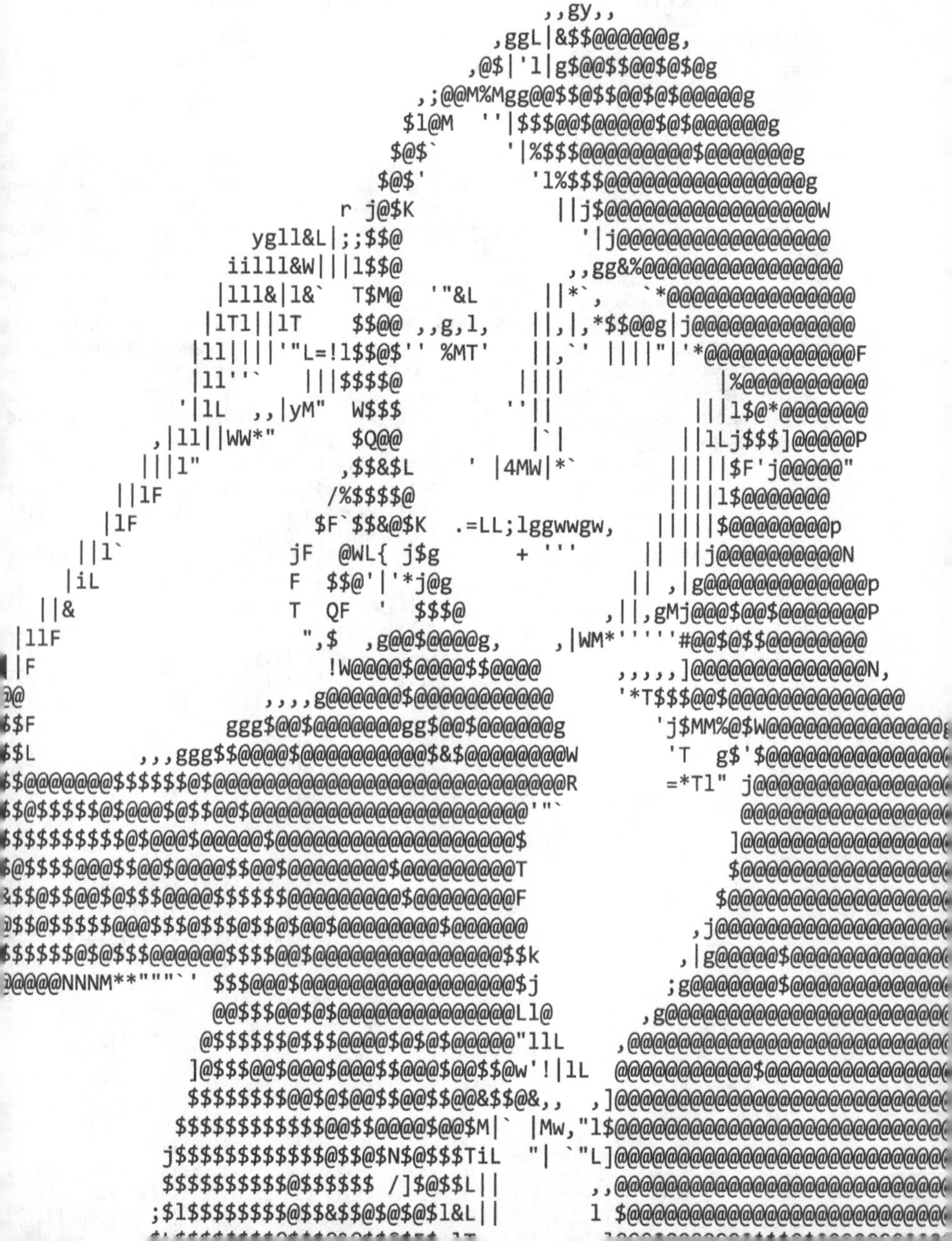

◀ **M.K. Sturdevant's** work has appeared in *Orion, Flyway, Slag Glass City,* and is forthcoming in *The Trumpeter.* In 2017, she was listed in the Top 25 Emerging Writers by *Glimmer Train Press.* She lives and works in the Chicago area.

Michele Flynn quit her day job to write sixteen years ago. She wanted to show her children that they could do what they loved. They lived on credit cards, her husband's schoolteacher salary, and stringer work. Now her day job is writing and she has branched out into travel writing (touristshellyb.com) and short stories. One of her sons is a writer, the other a musician. Both are doing what they love. ▼

▲ **Laura Rose**, an advertising copywriter and manager, lives in Bucks County, Pennsylvania with her husband and daughter. Her nonfiction has appeared in *Narrative, Memoir Journal,* and *Bucks County Writer.*

Molly Seale has most recently published essays in *Hippocampus Magazine* and *Hotel Amerika* as well as *ON YOUR OWN*, an anthology of poems and essays about widowhood. She holds an MFA in Theatre from the University of Texas and was a Fulbright-Hays grant recipient in the Performing Arts to the former Soviet Union. Her essay, "Illness," was included in Robert Atwan's Notable Essays and Literary Nonfiction of 2014. She lives in Makanda, Illinois. ▶

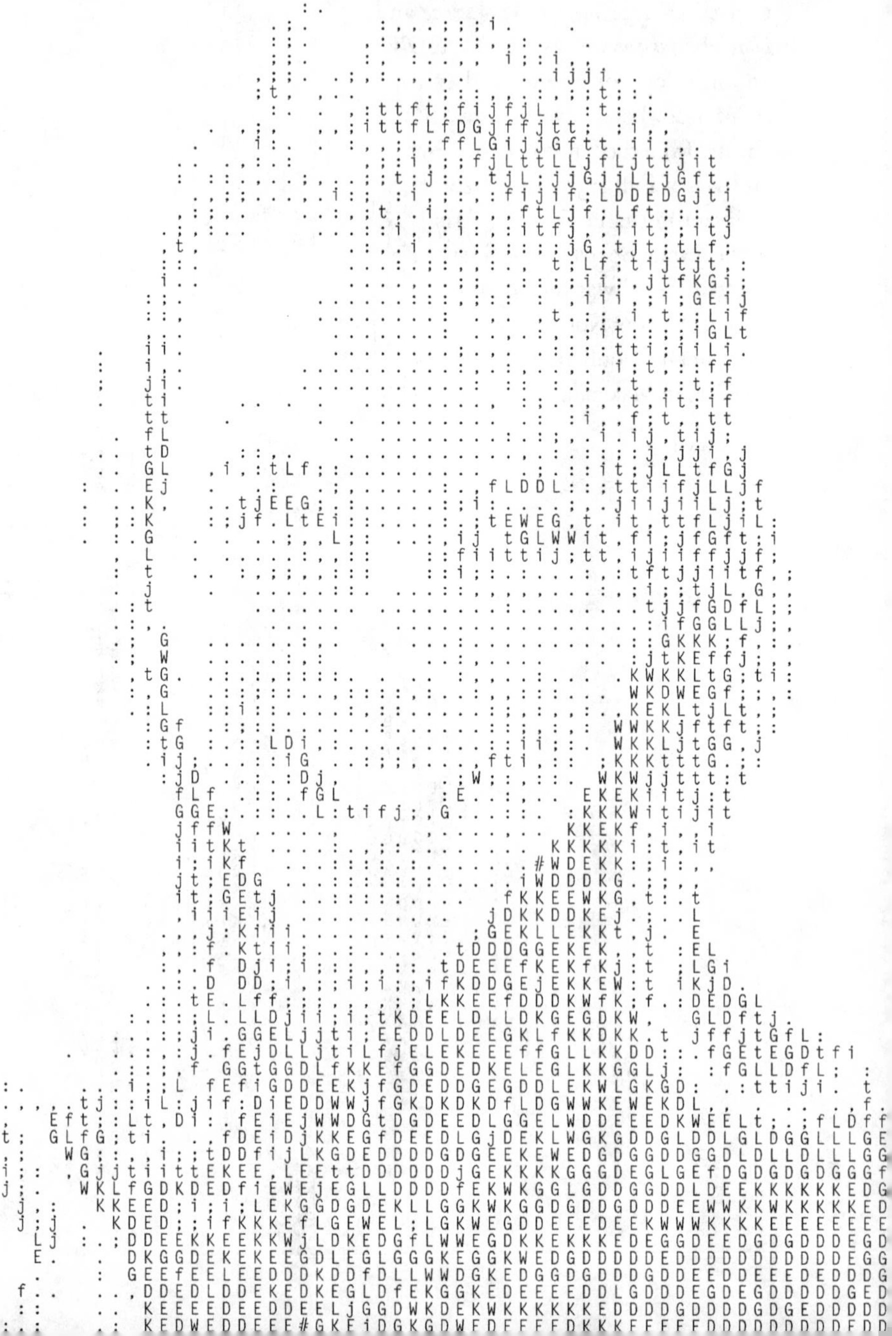

▲ **Annie Dawid's** three books of fiction are: *York Ferry, A Novel* (1993 Cane Hill Press); *Lily in the Desert: Stories* (2001: Carnegie-Mellon University Press Series in Short Fiction) and *And Darkness Was Under His Feet: Stories of a Family* (1998 Litchfield Review Press). Her book of poetry is: *Anatomie of The World* (2017).

◀ **Adrienne Garrison** is a writer, mother, and educator living in Bloomington, Indiana with her daughter and husband. She is currently working on her first novel and completing her MFA in Creative Writing with Pacific University in Oregon.

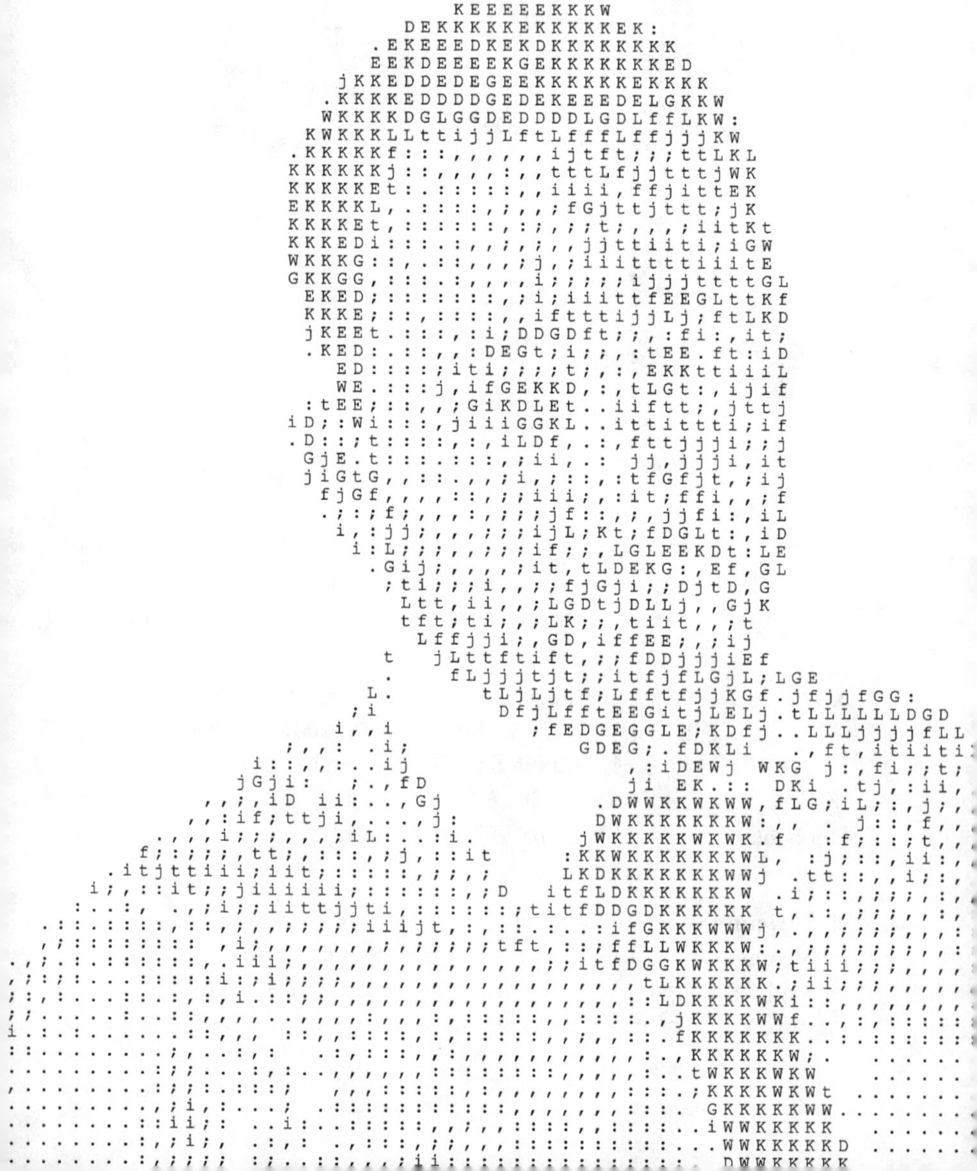

◀ **Jude Brewer's** writing has appeared in both the US and the UK through various lit journals, anthologies, and short films, including *New Millennium Writings, Fredericksburg Literary Review, Clackamas Literary Review, Scintilla Press,* and *Cultured Vultures.* He is the host and creator of *Storybound,* a podcast produced by Lit Hub Radio and The Podglomerate, a joint venture inspired from Jude's original literary "radio theatre" podcast, *Storytellers Telling Stories.*

Joanna Koch's short fiction has been published in *Dark Fuse, Hello Horror,* and the anthology *Game Fiction, Volume One.* This story's companion piece appears in the anthology *Trump: Utopia/Dystopia.* An MA Contemplative Psychotherapy graduate of Naropa University, Joanna works near Detroit as an advocate for women's rights. ▼

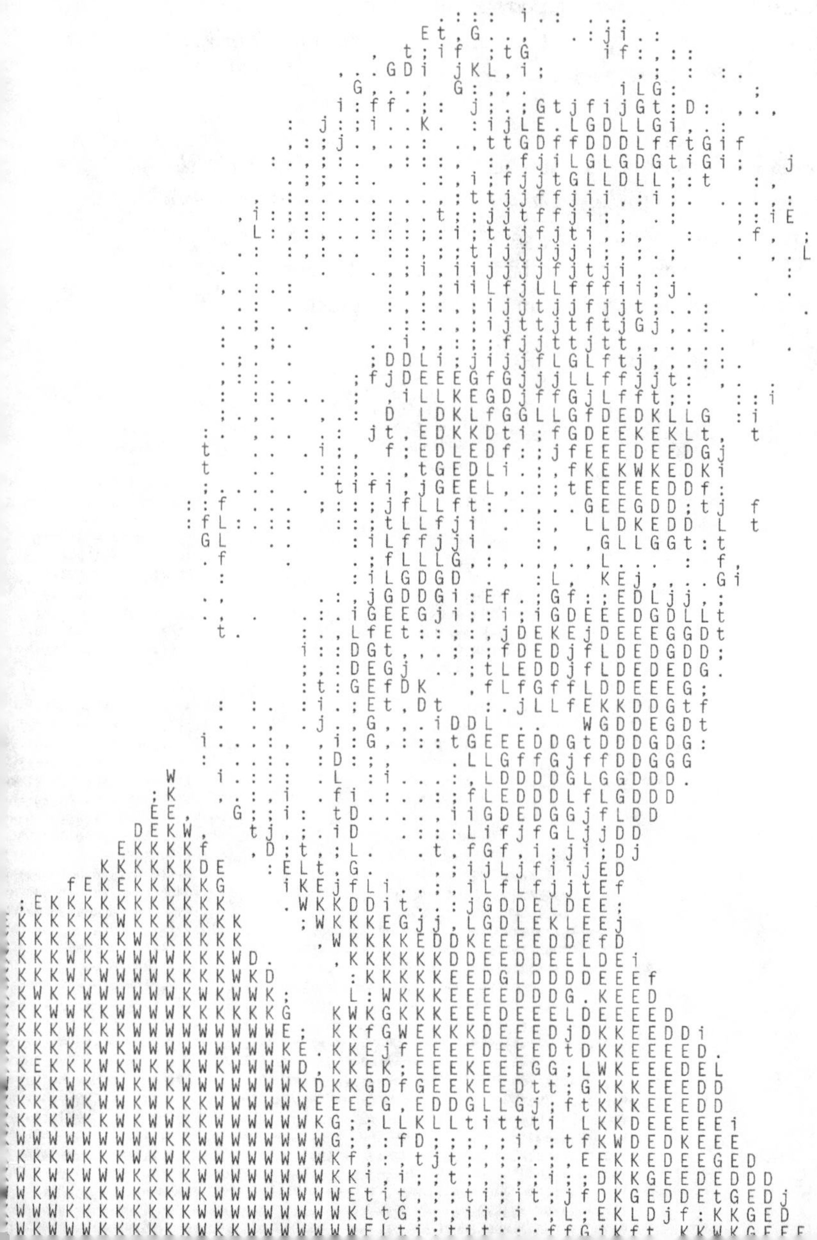

◀ **Brian Feehan** lives in Connecticut. He attended the Iowa Writer's Workshop summer program. He's had several short stories published, in the *Foundling Review* and *Plots with Guns,* and five plays published (Heuer Publishing), one of which was a finalist for the Heideman Award at the Actor's Theatre of Louisville.

Ginny Lowe Connors is the author of several poetry collections, including *Toward the Hanging Tree: Poems of Salem Village.* Connors has also edited poetry anthologies, including the recently published *Forgotten Women: A Tribute in Poetry.* The editor of *Connecticut River Review*, she also runs a small poetry press, Grayson Books. ▼

Kirk McDavitt is a writer on sabbatical from teaching writing, currently residing in Bucharest, Romania. In addition to writing short fiction and nonfiction, he is working on a novel (a fictionalized account of his experiences in a Vipassana meditation course). It will incorporate fifteen of his original songs. ▼

▲ **Jeanne Wilkinson** is a Brooklyn artist and writer. Her writing has been on NPR's *Living on Earth* and *Leonard Lopate Show*, and in *Columbia Journal, Digging Through the Fat*, and *Raven's Perch*, and her experimental videos featured at BAM, the Greenpoint and New York Independent Film Festivals, and 13th St. Repertory Theater.

▲ **Cezanne Alexander** is a storyteller. Her inexhaustible supply sources from escapades as a fly-fishing guide, ski instructor, Master Gardener, stock market analyst, options trader, CPA, beta-tester, ocean sailor, mountaineer, fantasy baseball commissioner, distance runner, insatiable reader, and prankster. Cezanne, her husband, and two blue heelers live in the Olympic rainforest.

*This is the author's first literary award and her
first work to appear in a print publication.*

▲ **Constance Campana** is a poet and essayist who lives in Attleboro, MA and teaches writing at Wheaton College. Recent publications have been in *Dogwood, 491 Magazine, Three Rivers Poetry Journal, Brown Journal of the Arts, Cleaver Magazine,* and *SNReview.*

▲ **Susan Maeder** lives on the North Coast of California and in southwestern France. She most recently performed her narrative poem, "The Goosefoot Tango," as a one woman show in France. A career highlight was receiving the annual poetry prize in 2014 from *New Millennium Writings*.

Natalie Mucker is a graduate student at Spalding University in Louisville, KY. She is working towards her MFA in creative writing. She is fond of animals, humans, yoga, creativity, kindness, all things food, and traveling—not necessarily in that order. ▶

This is the author's first literary award and her first work to appear in a print publication.

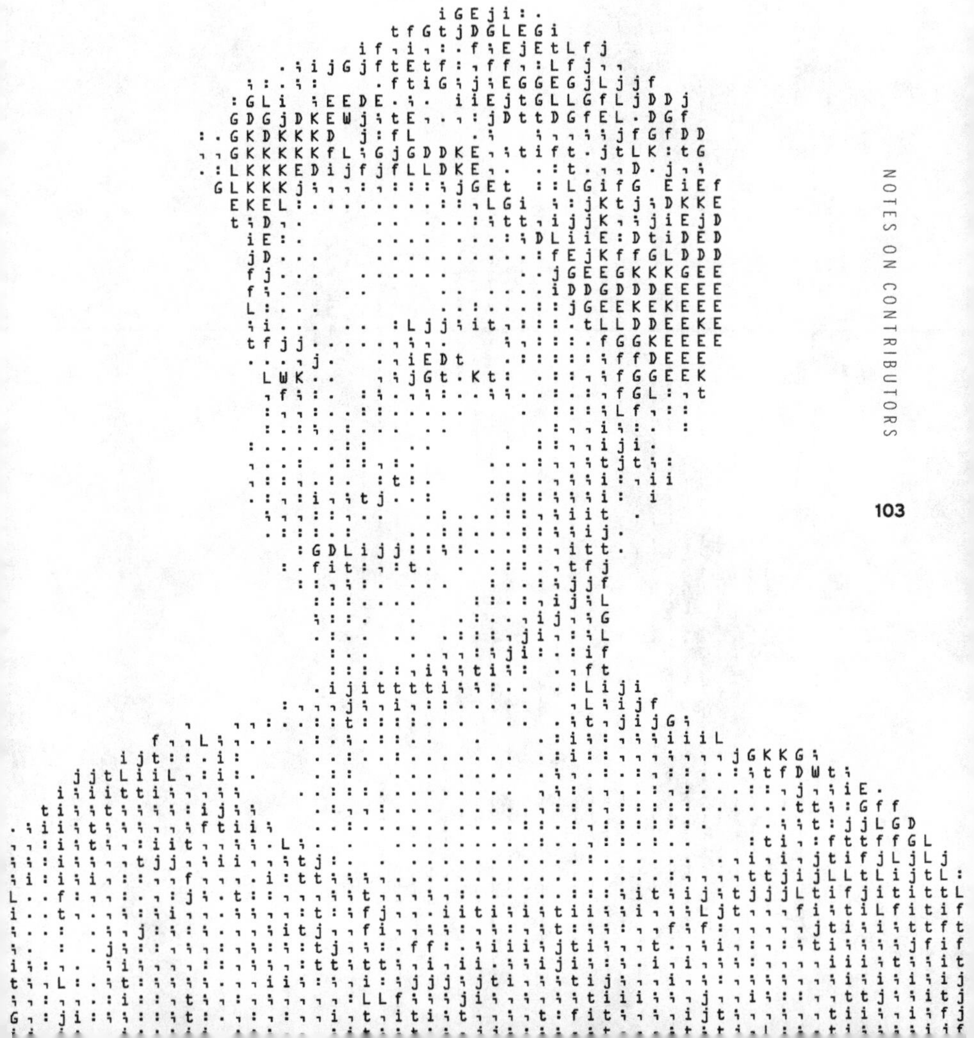

Keith Mark Gaboury earned a M.F.A. in creative writing from Emerson College. His poems have appeared in such publications as *Eclectica Magazine*, *Five 2 One Magazine*, and *New Millennium Writings*. After spending his days as a preschool teacher, Keith spends his nights writing poetry in San Francisco, California. ▼

▲ **Terri Trespicio** is a NY-based writer, speaker, and brand advisor. She earned her MFA in Creative Writing at Emerson College, has been a finalist for the Iowa Award, and won first place for nonfiction in *The Baltimore Review* in 2016. She is currently at work on her first book. territrespicio.com

Nina Gaby has been represented in numerous journals and anthologies, and currently focuses on the shorter form, using composites to illustrate the face of addiction and mental illness from an intimate perspective. Gaby is also a psychiatric nurse practitioner and a widely exhibited visual artist. ninagaby.wordpress.com ▼

This is the author's first literary award.

▲ **Kathryn Gahl** writes poetry, fiction, and nonfiction. "40" is from her memoir in verse, *DANCE WHEN YOU CAN'T*. Her works appear in over forty journals. A finalist at *Glimmer Train* and *Wisconsin People & Ideas*, she believes in the transcendent power of dark chocolate, deep sleep, and red lipstick.

Hana Rowan-Seddon (not pictured) is an 18 year old living near Brighton, UK. Taking a break from college has allowed her to focus more on her writing.

This is Hana's first literary award and her first
work to appear in a print publication.

REFINE|ENRICH
MUSEPAPER.ORG

The secret behind watershed moments of creative genius is the exponential growth catalyzed by small, continuous improvement. The Japanese call it kaizen.

Musepaper is *kaizen for writers*: an achievable monthly writing practice of 1,000 words or less, complimented with freshly curated writing prompts, easy submission, multiple publication opportunities (online *and* in print) and monthly writing awards administered by *New Millennium Writings,* the internationally recognized, prize-winning literary journal, creator of Sunshot Press and Musepaper.

There are many valuable tools for a writer's toolbox, but *kaizen writing* is the keystone, upon which all other tools depend on.

Refine your voice, enrich your style, and expand your creative faculty, faster and better, with a **Musepaper Writing Subscription.** Gift Subscriptions available upon request.

For a <u>limited-time</u>, take the cost of this book ($15) off any new annual subscription: CODE: **mpvol1rtk6f15**

musepaper.org

100% Independent • Ad-Free • Anti-Paywall

NMW+SUNSHOT+MUSEPAPER is not beholden to any boards, universities, or grants, governmental or otherwise. You will never be interrupted with paid advertising on any of our websites, in email newsletters, or in any of our print publications. The internet was supposed to make information, news, art, and literature available to the world, not put it behind paywalls.

We do our work solely for our contributors, submitters, and readers. We also don't believe in "unpaid interns," everyone who helps to make this possible is compensated.

NMW needs your help to ensure the future of literature is not homogenized and dumbed-down by the zero-sum game of private equity, big data, and corporate profit. It's a fight we can win, but it's a fight.

We'll keep showing up — NMW Literary Journal & Awards, Sunshot Press & Book Awards, Musepaper.org, and more — as long as you keep showing up.

We're constantly innovating to bring better opportunities and real encouragement to new, aspiring, and established writers. We push the envelope and we lick our own stamps.

Your support matters and we thank you.

With Love, Laughter, and Respect,

Dan   Alexis   **BRENT**

```
            {},                  ,'',
           jQrM,              @ "K
          F  "               @  %
         [    g*``"@        ]C`]
   gP"""Mw],  @*  ,#     ,g@,$pM@
   `k,  ,wrM]C          ]L ] ]C
         ]P              @  ]   @
      ,g@               $       @
    ,#`` "%*%,         ,]@,*`"wDw
```

Every *Musepaper 1.0* Paperback sold equals one (1) tree
planted in the Amazon Rainforest. See our reforestation
progress at musepaper.org/amazon. Thanks for your support.